TOURING NORTH AMERICA

SERIES EDITOR
Anthony R. de Souza, *National Geographic Society*

MANAGING EDITOR
Winfield Swanson, *National Geographic Society*

ACROSS THE APPALACHIANS

Washington, D.C., to Lake Michigan

BY
P. P. KARAN

AND
WILFORD A. BLADEN

RUTGERS UNIVERSITY PRESS • NEW BRUNSWICK, NEW JERSEY

This book is published in cooperation with the 27th International Geographical Congress, which is the sole sponsor of *Touring North America*. The book has been brought to publication with the generous assistance of a grant from the National Science Foundation/Education and Human Resources, Washington, D.C.

Rutgers University Press
109 Church Street
New Brunswick, New Jersey 08901

The paper used in this book meets the minimum requirements of American National Standard for Information Sciences—Permanence of Paper for Printed Library Materials, ANSI Z39.48-1984.

Library of Congress Cataloging-in-Publication Data

Karan, Pradyumna P. (Pradyumna Prasad)
    Across the Applachians: Washington, D.C. to Lake Michigan / by P. P. Karan and Wilford A. Bladen.
    p.   cm.—(Touring North America)
    Includes bibliographical references and index.
    ISBN 0-8135-1878-4 (cloth)—ISBN 0-8135-1879-2 (paper)
    1. Blue Ridge Mountains—Tours. 2. Northwest, Old—Tours. I. Bladen, Wilford A. II. Title. III. Series.
F217.B6K37   1992   92-10536
                                                                          CIP

First Edition

Frontispiece: Natural Bridge, Lexington, Virginia. Photograph courtesy of the Virginia Division of Tourism.

Series design by John Romer

Typeset by Peter Strupp/Princeton Editorial Associates

△ Contents

△ Foreword

Touring North America is a series of field guides by leading profes-
sional authorities under the auspices of the 1992 International
Geographical Congress. These meetings of the International Geographical Union (IGU) have convened every four years for over a
century. Field guides of the IGU have become established as significant scholarly contributions to the literature of field analysis. Their
significance is that they relate field facts to conceptual frameworks.

Unlike the last Congress in the United States in 1952, which had
only four field seminars, the 1992 IGC entails 13 field guides ranging
from the low latitudes of the Caribbean to the polar regions of
Canada, and from the prehistoric relics of pre-Columbian Mexico to
the contemporary megalopolitan eastern United States. This series
also continues the tradition of a transcontinental traverse from the
nation's capital to the California coast.

This guide is about the area that is the link between the urban-
ized eastern seaboard and the agricultural and industrial heart of
America. It is mainly north of the Ohio River and east of the
Mississippi, astride the Appalachian highland that stretches from
New England to Alabama. The transect crosses a diverse land of
historic and contemporary intricacy.

Wilford A. Bladen, a lifelong student of Appalachian culture and
economic and social problems associated with the coal-mining industry, is professor emeritus at the University of Kentucky. P. P. Karan,
professor of geography at the University of Kentucky, is a recognized
international scholar of cultural and economic development.

Anthony R. de Souza
BETHESDA, MARYLAND

△ Acknowledgments

This guidebook is a product of reconnaissance and field studies in the Atlantic Coastal Plain, the Applachians, and the eastern Great Lakes area. The various journeys afforded us an unusually extensive experience of changing cultural and economic patterns in this diverse region. We owe special to many individuals operating in various parts of the Appalachians and the Great Lakes. Many of the ideas expressed in this book evolved from discussions with these individuals, who are simply too numerous to list.

Cotton Mather guided us through many difficult moments in the preparation of the manuscript, as well as being a valuable sounding board for many of the ideas introduced. Significant contributions were made by Allen Noble of the University of Akron. We are also indebted to Hazel Karan and Ann Bladen for their support.

In addition, we acknowledge the dedicated work of the following cartographic interns at the National Geographic Society, who were responsible for producing the maps that appear in this book: Nikolas H. Huffman, cartographic designer for the 27th International Geographical Congress; Patrick Gaul, GIS specialist at COMSIS in Sacramento, California; Scott Oglesby, who drew the shaded relief artwork; Lynda Barker; Michael B. Shirreffs; and Alisa Pengue Solomon. Special thanks go to Susie Friedman of Computer Applications for procuring the hardware needed to complete this project on schedule.

We thank Lynda Sterling, publicity manager and executive assistant to Anthony R. de Souza, the series editor; Richard Walker, editorial assistant at the 27th IGC; and two geography interns at the National Geographic Society, Natalie Jacobus, who proofread the volume, and Tod Sukontarak, who indexed the volume. They were major players behind the scenes.

Many thanks, also, to all those at Rutgers University Press who had a hand in the making of this book, especially Kenneth Arnold, Karen Reeds, Marilyn Campbell, and Barbara Kopel.

Errors of fact, ommission, or interpretation are entirely our responsibility, and any opinions or interpretations are not necessarily those of the 27th International Geographical Congress, which is the sponsor of this field guide and the *Touring North America* series.

PART ONE

Introduction to the Region

Across the Appalachians

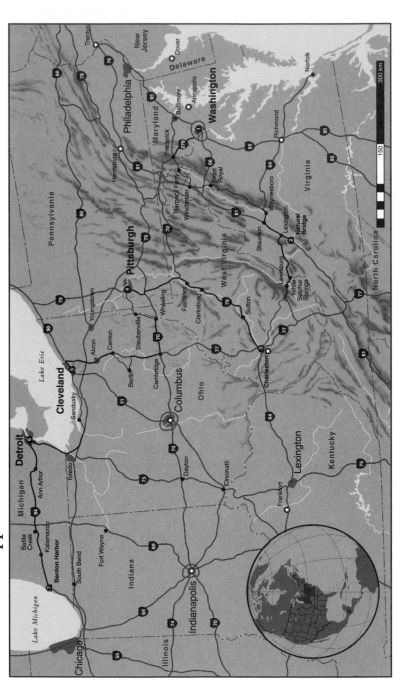

△ A Diverse Region

Six major physiographic regions comprise the eastern United States from Washington, D.C. to the Great Lakes—the Atlantic Coastal Plain, the Piedmont, the Blue Ridge, the Ridge and Valley Province, the dissected Appalachian Plateau, and the glaciated Great Lakes Plain. This segment of the country links the interior Middle Western states with the great port cities along the Atlantic. During the Colonial period, settlements sprang up along the Atlantic coast and became favored locations for assembling raw materials for export to England and France. For example, Georgetown, Washington's oldest neighborhood, was a port city that boasted a large harbor and warehouses filled with tobacco. Other port cities grew with the building of canals, roads, and railroads that connected the cities with the interior. In 1825 the opening of the Erie Canal made the area from the Great Lakes to the Appalachians a tributary to Atlantic port cities.

Later the New York Central Railroad, following the route of the Erie Canal, linked the Atlantic with Ohio and Michigan. Railroads integrated Ohio and Michigan into the economic life of the East by the middle of the nineteenth century, but the impact of the railroad transcended economics. It was also a social phenomenon, a symbol. It fed the American imagination with the lure of adventure and speed across the Appalachian mountain barrier.

The link function of this area is also borne out by the changes we have instituted. In 1956 the Federal Interstate Highway Act authorized the construction of a network of high-speed highways across the nation. Interstate highways now link the East with the Great Lakes region and areas farther west. These highways have changed traffic patterns around large cities and have affected many smaller towns along their routes. Moreover, major airlines use

Physiographic Regions

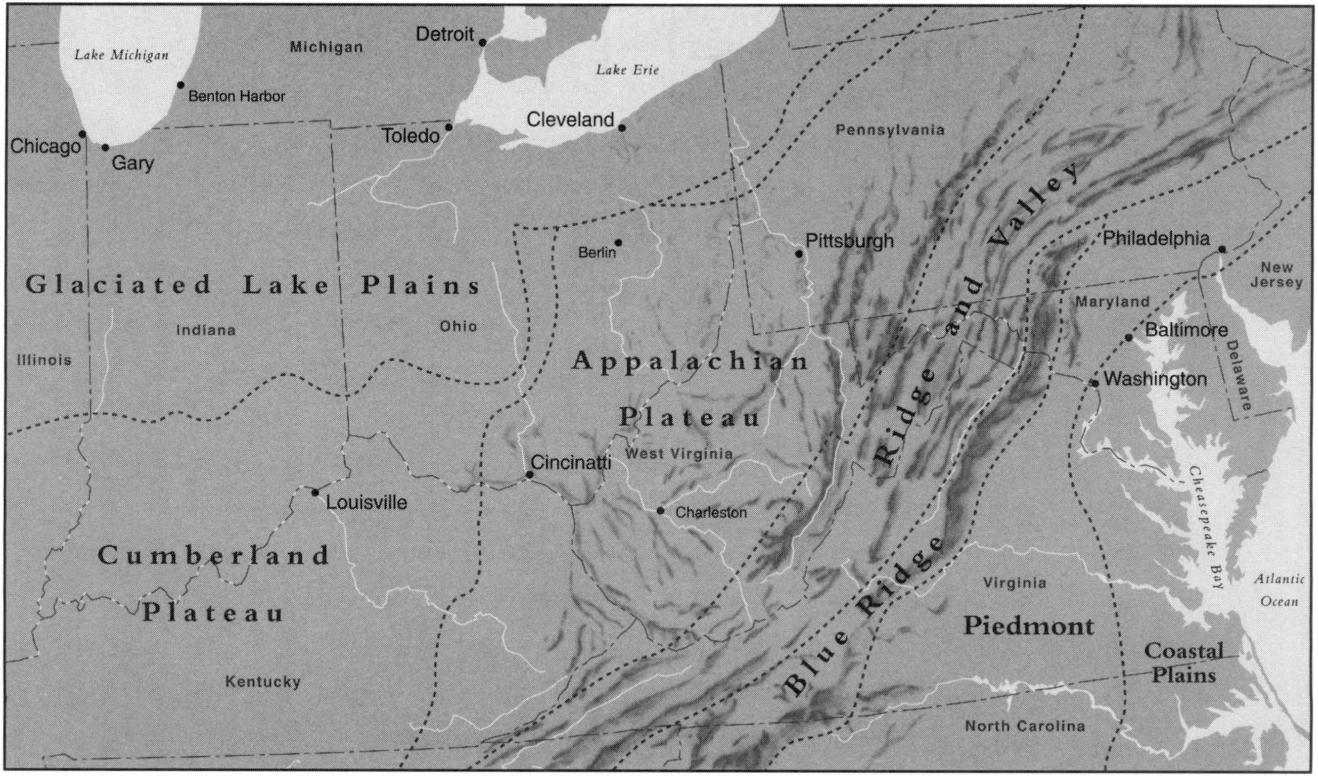

The White House, the oldest public building in Washington, D.C. Photograph courtesy of the Washington Convention and Visitors Association.

selected cities in this region as transportation hubs. For example, Pittsburgh serves as the hub for USAir.

Virginia's Front Royal highlights the link function. This inland port is really a train and truck terminal carved from 161 acres of pastureland. It is a collection point for freight transported by truck from the rich farm regions and industrial heartlands of Ohio, Michigan, and Illinois; the booming areas of northern Virginia; and the nearby states of West Virginia, Pennsylvania, Maryland, New York, and Delaware. The cargo is then moved by rail to seaports in the southeast corner of Virginia, where the facilities of Norfolk, Portsmouth, and Newport News—all run by the Virginia Port Authority—are linked together as the Port of Hampton Roads. Shippers traditionally move cargo through Baltimore because the

The American Core

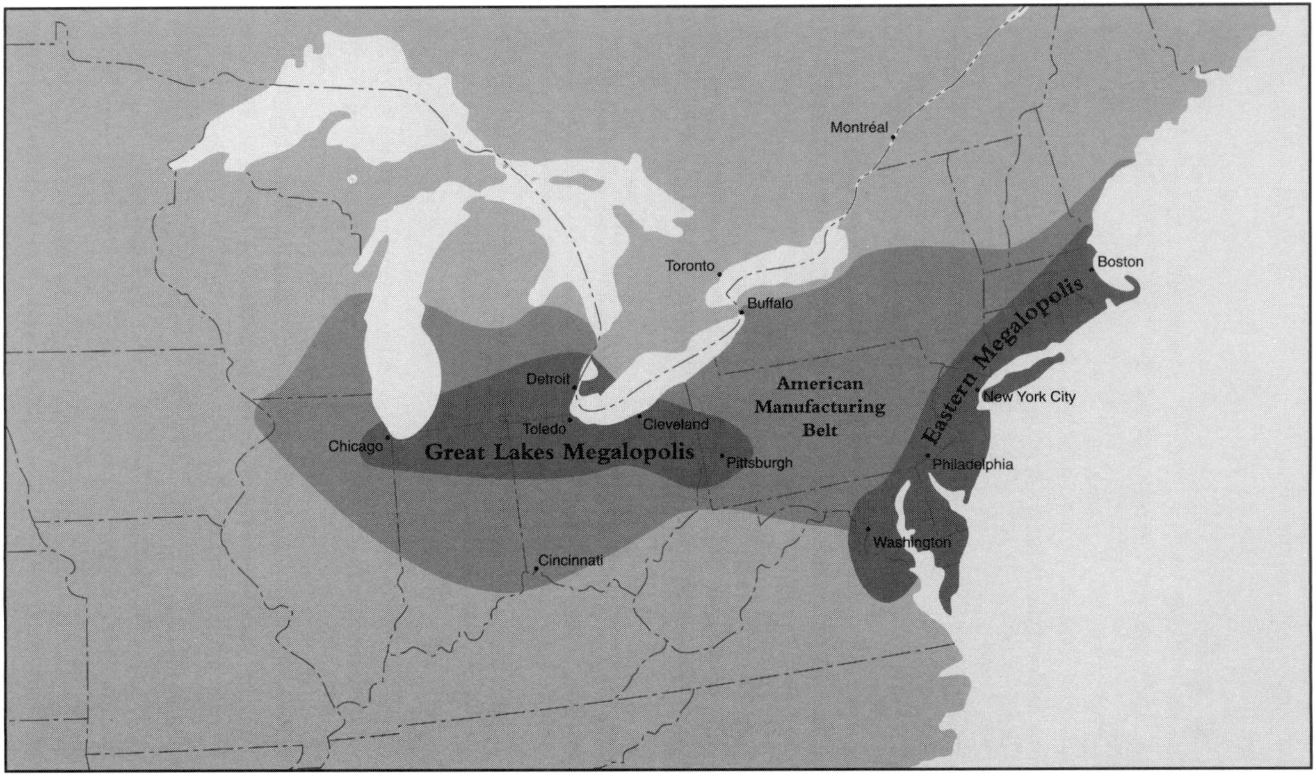

The American Core

Boston

New York City

Eastern Megalopolis

Philadelphia

Washington

Montréal

Buffalo

American Manufacturing Belt

Pittsburgh

Toronto

Cleveland

Great Lakes Megalopolis

Detroit

Toledo

Cincinnati

Chicago

overland distance is shorter and trucking costs are lower. However, steamship companies favor Norfolk because it is only 18 miles (two and one-half hours) from the Atlantic, a saving of 200 miles and as much as twelve hours of sailing time up the Chesapeake Bay to Baltimore.

This is an American core area. It contains the bulk of American settlement, population, economy, and political power. This core area encompasses a large part of the American Manufacturing Belt—a name coined to refer to the concentration of factories, foundries, and chemical plants that dot the area from the Atlantic to the Great Lakes. A major strength of this area lies in its concentration of corporate decision-makers—government and business executives, research scientists, and others—who affect industry, business, and commerce in the United States. Major cities here serve as headquarters for at least a third of the principal American corporations.

Growth trends indicate that the cities of the Great Lakes megalopolis may eventually extend across Appalachia and connect with the eastern megalopolis near Washington. This raises the future possibility of a supermegalopolis chain of cities extending from the Great Lakes to the East.

Major economic restructuring and social transformations are unfolding in this core region as the United States moves from the industrial to the post-industrial era. Technological changes and intensified global competition have decreased manufacturing employment. Technological developments have altered the value of proximity to large metropolitan areas for manufacturing firms. Improvements in transportation systems, the suburbanization of populations and housing, and the standardization of many production processes have allowed production sites to move away from metropolitan area markets. In general, manufacturing employment is decentralizing by moving out of central cities into the suburbs and out of metropolitan areas into nonmetropolitan areas. Major industrial centers along our route for this tour—such as Pittsburgh, Cleveland, Toledo, and Detroit—have experienced a decline in manufacturing employment and a redistribution of that employment from the central city into the suburbs.

Passage into a post-industrial society is marked by a change from producing goods to the rapid development of a service economy with increased employment in administration, finance, real estate, insurance, business services, legal services, research and development, and health care. Although resource-based manufacturing is still important in this region, the vitality and prosperity of this American core now lies in the science-based industries of the post-industrial era.

Many places in this section of the United States offer a glimpse into American political, cultural, and economic history. Frederick, Harpers Ferry, Winchester, and Lexington are associated with the Civil War. Many places here are linked with the life and work of George Washington. As a surveyor at the age of sixteen, he journeyed to the Shenandoah Valley. The last battle of the American Revolution was fought in 1782, when Fort Henry in Wheeling, (now) West Virginia, was attacked by a force of British soldiers and Indians. Charleston, West Virginia, is associated with the early American explorer, Daniel Boone; and Sandusky, Ohio, was explored by the French explorer La Salle in 1679.

Culturally, old ethnic neighborhoods such as those in Pittsburgh and Cleveland offer a cross section of nineteenth-century immigration and settlement patterns. Newer ethnic neighborhoods, such as those of the Arabs and Yemenis in Detroit, offer a glimpse of changing immigration and settlement patterns. In the Appalachians of West Virginia, we find descendants of early eighteenth-century settlers in the mountain valleys—part English, Irish, Scottish, Huguenot, and Cherokee.

The social geography of major metropolitan cities is changing. The downtown area—a cluster of high-rise office buildings, banks, and insurance companies—is surrounded by an inner city zone of old properties occupied by poor people, mostly minorities. This in turn is surrounded by middle-class suburbs where privacy and upward social mobility are emphasized. The major streets and highways in this zone have highway-oriented ribbon developments that serve the transient demands of the passing motorists. The most affluent groups are localized in the outer suburban ring and exurban areas.

One of the most significant developments is the profusion of near-identical shopping malls. Once restricted to the suburban edge, malls are now cropping up in the hearts of cities like Charleston, West Virginia. The success of the malls has perhaps as much to do with their entertainment value as it does with the convenience of having dozens of shops under one roof and a place to park, as well. They are airily designed with wide corridors, open areas, plants, and plenty of benches for the weary shopper. They offer a variety of diversions—from movie theaters, banks, restaurants, and skating rinks to arts, crafts, antiques, boats, cars, and dog and cat shows. They are places, as a new phrase has it, "to go malling"—to mosey, to see and be seen, to while away an hour or two among other human beings. Indeed, they have all but replaced Main Street, U.S.A., as America's marketplace and Saturday hangout. Teenagers love to congregate in them, and to many elderly folk they are a second home in which to eat, visit friends, and take their daily walk.

Major cities are synonymous with some of America's most famous innovators and entrepreneurs. Pittsburgh is associated with Andrew Carnegie and Andrew Mellon, Cleveland with John D. Rockefeller, Detroit with Henry Ford, and Battle Creek with W. K. Kellogg and C. W. Post. These entrepreneurs, along with many others, were responsible for the development of a wide range of industrial processes and business networks associated with the rise of industrial America and the achievement of a high mass-consumption society. Their names are also associated with charity and philanthropy, a more gentle part of the American national character.

PART TWO

The Itinerary

Washington, D.C., to Staunton, Virginia

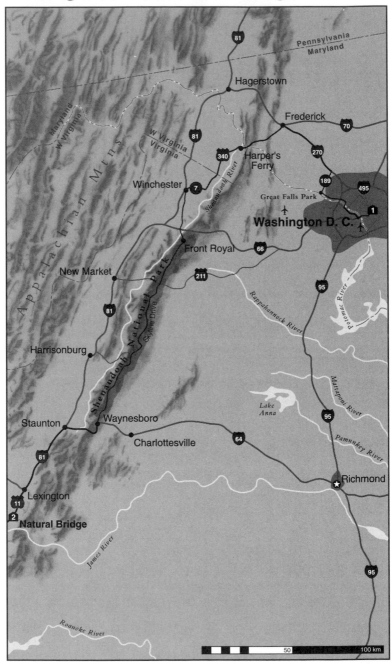

△ *Day One*

WASHINGTON, D.C., TO
NATURAL BRIDGE, VIRGINIA

Begin in downtown Washington at the Convention Center, Ninth and H streets.

The Convention Center (opened in 1983) pumped much-needed life into this part of the downtown by spurring the development of nearby hotels and office buildings.

Many of the public buildings in Washington are open to visitors and well worth a visit. A visitor information center is maintained at 1455 Pennsylvania Avenue (202-789-7000). Follow H Street west to New York Avenue and then move on to Pennsylvania Avenue at Fifteenth Street, N.W. To your left is the *Treasury Building,* the largest Greek Revival building in Washington.

Next to the Treasury Building is 1600 Pennsylvania Avenue, the President's house. It was officially named the *White House* by Congress in 1902 and is one of the oldest buildings in Washington. Part of it is open to the public (open Tuesdays to Saturdays, 10 a.m. to noon, telephone 202-456-7041 or 202-472-3669 for White House tours).

West of the White House is the *Old Executive Office Building,* built between 1871 and 1888. Patterned after the Louvre, it originally housed the War, Navy, and State Departments. Now it houses the Office of the Vice President of the United States, the Office of Management and Budget, and the National Security Council. Many historic events have taken place in this building. Here in the 1980s Oliver North and Fawn Hall shredded Iran–Contra documents.

View of Washington, D.C., looking west. The Library of Congress and the U.S. Supreme Court are in the left foreground, and the Senate Office Building faces the Capitol (center). Pennsylvania Avenue runs west from Union Station (right). Photograph courtesy of the Washington Convention and Visitors Association.

Across the street from the White House is Lafayette Square. During the War of 1812 and the Civil War, soldiers camped in the square. Today protesters use the space to set up their placards. In each corner is a statue of a foreign general who came to the colonies to help fight the Revolution—Lafayette, Rochambeau, Steuben, and Kosciusko. A statue of Andrew Jackson stands in the center of the square. The green canopy at 1651 Pennsylvania Avenue marks the entrance to Blair House, the residence used by heads of state during official visits to Washington.

The White House sits on the promontory of one of a series of riverine terraces that form the southeastern part of the District of Columbia, which is part of the Atlantic Coastal Plain. As we continue west on Pennsylvania Avenue the land rises to the northwest. We cross *Rock Creek,* which has cut a deep gorge and flows south into the Potomac. Rock Creek tumbles through a 4-mile-long pastoral park; a parkway runs the length of it. On weekends some park roads are closed to traffic for the use of cyclists, joggers, and walkers. Designated a national "pleasure ground" by Congress in 1890, Rock Creek Park was a favorite spot of Theodore Roosevelt, who rode horses here.

After crossing Rock Creek, we enter *Georgetown,* the capital's wealthiest neighborhood. Settled in the early 1700s, Georgetown's position as the navigational head of the Potomac made it a major port for the shipment of tobacco grown in Maryland. In 1789 the state granted the town a charter, but two years later George Washington included Georgetown in the Territory of Columbia, site of the new capital. Tobacco eventually became less important, and Georgetown became a milling center, using water power from the Potomac. When the Chesapeake and Ohio Canal, south of M Street, was completed in 1850, Georgetown intensified its milling operations and became the eastern end of the waterway that stretched 184 miles to the west. After 1870, the canal could not compete with the railroads. Now the canal and towpath are a National Historical Park, ideal for hiking, biking, and canoeing. (Information can be obtained from the C & O Historical Park, P.O. Box 4, Sharpsburg, MD 21782, telephone 202-443-0024.)

Besides the canal (between Jefferson and 31st streets), streets off Wisconsin Avenue house the city's social and political elite in beautifully restored townhouses with lush gardens and lovely magnolia trees. Today Georgetown's zoning laws, which are among the city's strictest, are designed to preserve the historic character of the area.

Georgetown owes some of its charm and unique personality to its geography. The town-unto-itself is separated from Washington to the east by Rock Creek, on the south by the bordering Potomac, and on the west by Georgetown University. The whole area is

Historic Georgetown, Washington, D.C. Photograph courtesy of the Washington Convention and Visitors Association.

well-suited to strolling and a walk up either M Street or Wisconsin Avenue will take you past a dizzying array of stores, with merchandise ranging from expensive antiques, jewelry, and the latest fashions to records.

Continue west on M Street and cross *Key Bridge* into Rosslyn, Virginia. The bridge is named after Francis Scott Key, author of the national anthem. South of Rosslyn lies Arlington National Cemetery and the Pentagon, headquarters of the Department of Defense. *Arlington National Cemetery* and the *Pentagon* make an enjoyable half day of sightseeing. While not the largest cemetery in the country, Arlington is perhaps the best known, a place where visitors can trace America's history through the aftermath of its battles. It contains the grave of President John F. Kennedy, the Tombs of the Unknowns, and many others. The Robert E. Lee

Memorial is in the cemetery and the Marine Corps Memorial is nearby. The cemetery is open daily (telephone, 703-557-0613). For tours of the Pentagon, telephone 202-695-1776.

Proceed north of Rosslyn on the scenic George Washington Memorial Parkway along the Potomac past McLean, Virginia, headquarters of the Central Intelligence Agency. To reach the Maryland side of Great Falls Park we cross the Potomac and follow MacArthur Boulevard. The twin parks of Great Falls— on either side of the Potomac River, 13 miles northwest of Georgetown—are part of the National Park System. The steep, jagged falls roar into a narrow gorge, providing one of the most spectacular scenic attractions in the East (telephone 703-285-2966 for the Virginia side; 301-299-2026 for the Maryland side).

High-Tech Corridor to Frederick, Maryland, 25 miles, I-270

Falls Road (Route 189) leads to Interstate 270 and on to Frederick, Maryland. Along Interstate 270, a corridor of high-tech industries has developed during the last twenty years. Similar high-tech corridors have also emerged along Interstate 95 (both north and south of the Beltway), as well as on the Dulles Airport Access Road. Research and development labs, offices, and clean industries dominate these corridors. The commercial landscape is characterized by large lots—usually several acres—and includes large-scale structures, extensive on-site parking, and generous landscaped parks.

Along I-270 between Bethesda and Gaithersburg, officially designated as the Technology Corridor by the state of Maryland, biotechnology industries are dominant. Anchored by the National Institutes of Health, the Bureau of Standards, the U.S. Agricultural Center, the Food and Drug Administration, and the U.S. Patent and Trademark Office, a full-fledged high-tech corridor has emerged.

Frederick: A Masterpiece in Maryland

The historic town of *Frederick* (population, 21,000) is noted for its handsome eighteenth- and nineteenth-century buildings. These buildings, together with the surrounding country houses, farms, factories, and schools, illustrate how the town stretched and diversified. It is the classic American palette of home, church, school, and work, an architectural portrait that has evolved over the last 240 years.

Frederick saved its hundreds of antebellum buildings from being burned to the ground by paying $200,000 to Confederate General Jubal Early on 9 July 1864. The money was borrowed from five local banks, which financed the loan with bond issues; the last payment was made on 1 October 1951.

Unlike historic towns, whose polite demeanor vanished with the invasion of chain stores and fast-food restaurants, life in this small but urbane county seat has maintained its grace and dignity. Activities during weekdays center around the courthouse, City Hall, and the two historic shopping streets, Market and Patrick. The city today is a manufacturing and service center for the surrounding community. It is well-known for its antique shops. Galleries featuring work by local artists and artisans flourish here, as does the favorite candy store, a chocolatier à la New York. Moderately priced lunches are still served on sparkling white tablecloths at such restaurants as the popular Brown Pelican (5 East Church Street, telephone 301-695-5833). Banks, which had underwritten the Civil War loans, now occupy costly neo-classical and Art Deco buildings.

In Frederick, old buildings are generally reused, not replaced, and new construction echoes rather than mimics the past. The large contemporary County Court House, for example, was built with the red brick that is favored in Frederick, but was discreetly set back from the street. In 1986 City Hall offices moved into the old courthouse, a rugged Italianate landmark on Court House Square. On the second floor you will find a fine example of antebellum folk art, a hand-sewn tattered American flag with thirty-four stars painted on a blue field (indicating that it was made sometime after 1861, when Kansas was admitted to the Union).

History books credit Daniel Dulaney, a prominent lawyer, politician, and land speculator, as the founder of Frederick in 1745. Wagonloads of pioneers heading west from Baltimore rumbled down what is now Patrick Street, a route that in 1818 became National Road, the nation's first federal highway.

Like other developers, Dulaney attracted settlers by donating land for churches. By 1746 the Lutherans occupied a temporary log building on East Church Street, where their present parsonage stands, and the Anglicans occupied the first All Saint's Church on the street which still bears its name. Though the British became the ruling party, German was the language most commonly heard on Frederick's streets, and documents were often written in both English and German.

The continuing process of accommodating the present to the past often takes odd forms. The old tombstone embedded in the stone wall behind the Lutheran church and the *trompe l'oeil* bird escaping from a window on Nicole's turn-of-the-century shop on Market Street are just two. Each enhances the reassuring sense of continuity and timelessness that pervades Frederick.

Mount Olivet Cemetery at the south end of Market Street contains the graves of Francis Scott Key and his wife; Barbara Fritchie, whom John Greenleaf Whittier immortalized; and more than 400 unknown Confederate soldiers, killed in Civil War battles.

Tour guides and maps of Frederic's historic district are available at the main Visitor Information Center, 19 East Church Street (telephone 301-663-8687).

The Blue Ridge and the Shenandoah Valley

HARPERS FERRY, WEST VIRGINIA

Proceeding on Route 340, 15 miles southwest of Frederick we enter the Blue Ridge. The *Harpers Ferry* (population, 360) water gap is where the Potomac River flows across the Blue Ridge. The town of Harpers Ferry is at the western edge of this gap at the

Harpers Ferry, West Virginia. Photograph courtesy of the Virginia Division of Tourism.

confluence of the Potomac and Shenandoah rivers, where West Virginia and Maryland meet.

The water gap at Harpers Ferry served as one of the major travel routes across the Blue Ridge during the early history of the United States. A 0.5-mile walking tour through the Harpers Ferry National Historical Park (Shenandoah Street) links several restored homes, a gun-making museum, the engine house (where abolitionist John Brown was caught), a blacksmith shop, a confectionery, a tavern, and Jefferson Rock, which commands an excellent view of the rivers and hills. Harpers Ferry National Historical Park is an area composed of five separate tracts of land for a total of about 2,500 acres in Virginia, West Virginia, and Maryland. The park is open year-round except Christmas Day. Admission is $5 for each carload or $2 for individuals (304-535-6371).

Because of its location, Harpers Ferry is a popular recreation area. The Appalachian Trail passes nearby, and the Shenandoah and Potomac rivers offer opportunities for fishing, canoeing, and rafting. If you are attracted to scenic rivers, you can join a Shenandoah River whitewater rapids expedition at Harpers Ferry. Each trip takes five hours, including a Southern hospitality-style picnic. The Blue Ridge Outfitters in Harpers Ferry (304-725-3444) or Front Royal Canoe Company (703-665-5440) organize the trips between April and November.

Harpers Ferry was named for Robert Harper, who bought the site in 1747 and operated the first ferry boats across the Potomac and Shenandoah rivers. John Brown was tried and hanged at Charles Town, West Virginia (population, 3,000) (not to be confused with Charleston) about 5 miles south of Harpers Ferry. Charles Town is also famous for horseracing; the Charles Town Races originated in 1786. And, the first rural free delivery of mail in the United States started at Charles Town in 1896.

WINCHESTER, VIRGINIA

From Harpers Ferry, take U.S. Route 340 south to Berryville, Virginia, in the northern part of the Shenandoah Valley. Here we will turn west on Virginia Route 7 and follow it for approximately 8 miles to *Winchester,* Virginia (population 20,000).

Winchester occupies a key location on the linkage route between the Atlantic Coastal Plain and the interior of the United States. The Appalachian Uplands, between the Piedmont and the Ohio Valley, is divided naturally. The western part, through the Allegheny–Cumberland Plateau, has layers of rock that are nearly horizontal, and streams that cut back into it in all directions. Strata in the eastern part are folded so that the surface has become a multitude of ridges and valleys. One of these Appalachian valleys is much wider and longer than the rest and is called the Great Valley. It extends for more than 1,000 miles, from the St. Lawrence River valley in the north to central Alabama in the south. Although it includes parts of seven states, its total area is only about 20,000 square miles, because its width rarely exceeds 25 miles and often is less. The Great Valley has different local names and is drained by a number of streams, including the Potomac and Shenandoah rivers. In northern Virginia the valley is known as the Shenandoah Valley or the Valley of Virginia. The valley is walled on both sides by sharp ridges known to residents as North Mountain and the Blue Ridge. In early days the mountains barred east–west movement, but the valley served as a great north–south highway. Streams of migrating settlers drove their wagons down the valley to the boundary of what is now Tennessee and then back north through Cumberland Gap into Kentucky. This explains why Kentucky rather than Ohio became the first state west of the Allegheny Mountains. The importance of the topography of the Great Valley was illustrated by troop movements north and south during the Civil War. Winchester was caught in a key location between opposing forces and changed hands seventy-two times during the Civil War. The First, Second, and Third Battles of Winchester occurred in 1862, 1863, and 1864. The Confederate and National cemeteries contain the bodies of 7,500 Union and Confederate soldiers who died in these battles. Winchester today is still an important crossroads with numerous facilities for travelers.

You can visit the George Washington Office-Museum at the corner of South Braddock and West Cork Streets, which served as Washington's office during 1755 to 1756 and houses relics of the French, Indian, Revolutionary, and Civil Wars (telephone 703-662-4412).

An early landlord in the Shenandoah Valley, George Washington required each tenant to plant four acres of apples. Today extensive apple orchards surround Winchester, and the Shenandoah Valley is one of America's outstanding apple-growing areas. In early fall, the air is redolent with the earthy smells of fresh-cut hay, roadside flowers, and ripening apples. Even before the summer foliage changes color, the advent of fall is evident in the fields of ripening pumpkins, odd-shaped winter squash, and multi-colored Indian corn. Down every country road, or so it seems, there is yet another orchard, the trees heavy with nature's bright jewels. Every farmer's market overflows with baskets of apples in tones of deep red or golden yellow. Others are a warm blush or pink or orange speckled with russet.

SHENANDOAH'S APPLE HARVEST

With 11 million bushels harvested annually, the *Shenandoah Valley* and adjacent areas rank as the sixth largest apple-producing region in America. Main varieties include Golden Delicious, Red Delicious, Rome Beauty, Jonathan, York Imperial, and Red Stayman. Varieties that are not considered commercially viable are grown in the smaller orchards and can be found at festivals and roadside stands: Rambo, Grimes Golden, Winesap, Newton Pippin, and Black Twig. Gala, Fuji, and Ginger Gold, which are good all-purpose apples and delicious to eat, are making an impact in the valley.

One way to enjoy the different varieties of apples is to visit some of the apple festivals during September and October. One of the major festivals is the Winchester Apple Harvest Arts and Crafts Festival in mid-September (telephone 703-665-8060). There are stalls selling apple chutneys and relishes, jellies and jams, jugs of fresh-pressed cider, and pies that came out of someone's oven that morning. Your nose may lead you to a vendor who is making apple doughnuts rolled in fine sugar. If doughnuts are not to your taste, you'll perhaps succumb to a slice of bread topped with warm apple butter that's been cooked down by an eager group belonging to the Four-H Club. Aspiring contestants in apple-pie-baking and butter-making enter the Virginia State Championships at the festival in Winchester. Entertained by live music and clogging, visitors to this two-day event can also buy or at least examine all manner of handmade crafts.

One mile north of Winchester on Route 522 is a big red barn called the Virginia Farm Market. Here shelves and tables groan under all sorts of apple products, including apple butter and apple cider you jug for yourself. Most of the apples grown in this region are sold wholesale to supermarkets and to canning and processing plants. At the National Fruit Product Company processing plant, for example, apples are made into vinegar, apple sauce, apple butter, and sweet cider, and sold nationally under the White House label.

Apple products made in the Shenandoah Valley are available in retail stores or by mail order. There are some excellent apple butters on the market, including one by the Bowman Apple Products Company in Mount Jackson (telephone 703-477-311), made from apples grown in their own orchards. Sold under the label Old Virginia, this apple butter is thick, rich tasting, and dark with spices. Yet another, sweetened with their own maple syrup, is prepared by September Morn Organic Farms (Route 624, Doe Hill, telephone 703-396-6219).

Another specialty you may want to try are dried apple slices. The owners of L'Esprit De Campagne (P.O. Box 3130, Winchester, Virginia 22601, telephone 703-722-4224) dry York apple wedges, pitted cherries, and tomato halves. The Shenandoah Candy Company (1625 Amherst Street, Winchester, Virginia 22601, telephone 703-662-3538) sells apple candy—sweet confections sometimes blended with chocolate and flavored with mint, cinnamon, apricot, or orange. They sell apple syrup as well, which is available from local country stores, some roadside markets, or by mail order.

A nonalcoholic sparkling cider called Alpenglow is processed by the Linden Beverage Company (Route 1, Box 35, Linden, Virginia 22642, telephone 703-635-2118), just a few miles east of Front Royal on Route 55. The cider comes in five flavorful blends.

Seven miles south of Winchester on Route 522 you are within easy reach of the town of White Post on Route 340. Visitors who plan ahead can dine and enjoy an overnight stay at L'Auberge Provencale, a six-room inn set in the shadow of the Blue Ridge Mountains.

Skyline Drive and Shenandoah National Park, 105 miles, I-81, I-66

From Winchester, go south on Interstate 81 to its intersection with Interstate 66 near Strasburg, Virginia, and turn back east for approximately 12 miles to Front Royal, at the northern entrance to Shenandoah National Park.

Shenandoah is an Indian name thought to mean "Daughter of the Stars." The park is in one of the highest and most beautiful and historic regions of the eastern United States. It extends approxi-

Shenandoah National Park, Virginia. Photograph courtesy of the Virginia Division of Tourism.

mately 80 miles along the crest of the Blue Ridge Mountains, from Front Royal in the north to near Waynesboro in the south. Spur ridges from the mountain crest blend into the rolling land of the Shenandoah Valley on the west and the wooded hills, orchards, and fields of the Piedmont on the east. Between the ridges are deep, timbered hollows and cascading streams. *Skyline Drive*, south from Front Royal, occupies the ridgecrest the entire length of the park. At intervals along the drive are overlooks that afford excellent views of the mountains. Near Thornton Gap the route passes through a 700-foot tunnel. Skyline Drive can be entered at Front Royal, at Thornton Gap, between Luray and Sperryville, on U.S. Route 211; at Swift Run Gap between Stanardsville and

Elkton on U.S. Route 33; and at Rockfish Gap between Charlottesville and Waynesboro on U.S. 250/I-64. A speed limit of 35 miles per hour must be observed in the park. For persons continuing south, the Blue Ridge Parkway extends another 469 miles from the southern end of Skyline Drive.

Shenandoah National Park is a wildlife sanctuary with a large variety of animals, birds, and reptiles. It contains more than 100 species of trees and about 1,200 species of flowering plants. In spring the redbud and dogwood, azaleas and mountain laurel are spectacular. The park headquarters is approximately 4 miles west of Thornton Gap on U.S. 211. Visitors' centers are located at Big Meadows (Milepost 51) and Dickey Ridge (Milepost 4.6). Here may be seen movies depicting the history and establishment of the park and museum exhibits devoted to the history and culture of the mountain area.

Between Front Royal and Swift Run Gap (66 miles, or 106 kilometers), three main types of rocks crop out in roadcuts and cliffs. These are greenstone, granite, and sandstone. The floor of the Great Valley to the west is primarily limestone. Greenstone is a basalt that has been transformed by heat and pressure. It occurs from the park's north entrance to Lands Run Gap Skyline Drive. In this area, overlooks to the west provide a panorama of the South Fork of the Shenandoah River, Massanutten Mountain, and in the far distance on clear days, Little North Mountain and Great North Mountain. The West Virginia state line runs along the rear flank of Little North Mountain.

From Thornton Gap to Stony Man overlook, Skyline Drive is on granite. Most of the mountains to the east are carved out of granite. Stony Man overlook provides a view of Luray to the west, famous for its limestone caverns. The tree-covered ridges on the west side of the Blue Ridge are cut from sandstone. The view from Black Rock, just west of Big Meadows Lodge, is one of the most spectacular along the entire Skyline Drive. Much of the length of Massanutten Mountain is visible and on clear days, so is Little North Mountain beyond. From Swift Run Gap to Rockfish Gap, (39 miles, or 63 kilometers), the route crosses a variety of geologic formations of greenstone, sandstone, and granite. Rockfish Gap marks the southern end of Skyline Drive and the northern end of the Blue Ridge Parkway. The change from one route to the other is one of administration, not of geology.

The Shenandoah National Park has more than 500 miles of trails for hiking and horseback riding. Picnic areas at seven locations have water, fireplaces, tables, and restrooms. Permits are needed for camping. Admission to the park is $5 for a private car or $2 per person (call 703-999-2229; or 703-989-2266 for taped information on the weather and activities). If you visit in the fall, plan to attend the annual Festival of Leaves held in Front Royal the second or third weekend in October, when the foliage is usually at its peak. The festival offers a variety of attractions, including crafters and an art show with over fifty artists exhibiting. Contact: Chamber of Commerce, P.O. Box 568, Front Royal, Virginia 22630, telephone 703-635-3185.

Staunton to Natural Bridge, Virginia, 50 miles, I-64, I-81

Leave Shenandoah National Park and Skyline Drive near Waynesboro and turn west on I-64 to *Staunton* (population, 21,900). One of the oldest cities west of the Blue Ridge, it was named for Lady Staunton, the wife of Governor William Gooch. Staunton was not damaged during the Civil War and has one of Virginia's finest collections of nineteenth-century architecture. Staunton was also the birthplace and home of President Woodrow Wilson, the U.S. President during World War 1. A museum houses his memorabilia (telephone 703-885-0897 for information). Set in the fertile Shenandoah Valley fields and orchards, between the Blue Ridge and the Allegheny mountain ranges, the area around Staunton is noted for poultry, livestock, and wool.

LEXINGTON, VIRGINIA

From Staunton we go south on I-81, past Steele's Tavern near where Cyrus McCormack was born and where he perfected his first reaper, and on to *Lexington* (population, 6,900), the home of Washington and Lee University and Virginia Military Institute.

Woodrow Wilson Birthplace, Staunton, Virginia. Photograph courtesy of the Virginia Division of Tourism.

Virginia Military Institute (founded in 1839) is noted for the excellence of its military and academic programs. VMI graduates have played important roles in every U.S. military confrontation since the Mexican War of 1846. General Stonewall Jackson taught at VMI for ten years before the Civil War. Union forces shelled and burned the institute during the Civil War. General George C. Marshall was a VMI graduate. The George C. Marshall Museum and Library is at the west end of the parade ground. It houses General Marshall's personal papers and material relating to U.S. military and diplomatic history. The Nobel Peace Prize awarded to General Marshall in 1953 is on display. Admission is free (703-463-7103). Among other places of interest on the campus is Jack-

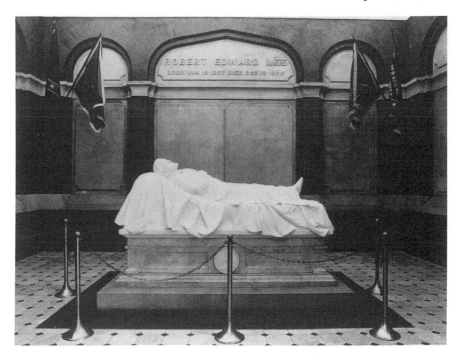

Lee Chapel on the campus of Washington and Lee University, Lexington, Virginia. Photograph courtesy of the Virginia Division of Tourism.

son Memorial Hall, the cadet assembly hall, which is dominated by an oil painting of the VMI cadet charge at the Battle of New Market. The lower level of Jackson Memorial Hall houses the VMI Museum, which contains items that illustrate the history and traditions of the institute.

General Robert E. Lee was president of *Washington and Lee* (founded in 1749) from the close of the Civil War until his death in 1870. The colonnaded buildings of its campus are especially attractive. General Lee designed the president's house. The stable used by his horse, Traveller, is behind the house. Lee Chapel was built in 1867 under the general's supervision. It contains his office, just as he left it on 30 September 1870. Lee and his family are buried beneath the chapel on the museum level.

Stonewall Jackson House, Lexington, Virginia. Photograph courtesy of the Virginia Division of Tourism.

Other attractions in Lexington include Lawyers Row and Court House Square, which were laid out as part of the original town in 1778, and the Stonewall Jackson house and garden at 8 East Washington Street.

Leave Lexington and continue south on I-81, approximately 17 miles to Natural Bridge.

Natural Bridge, Virginia, to Charleston, West Virginia

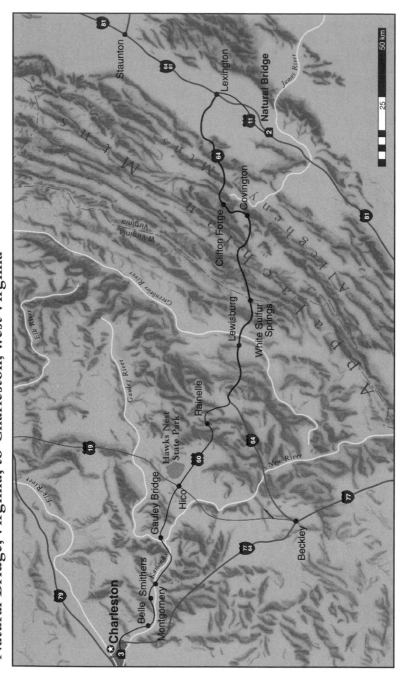

△ Day Two

NATURAL BRIDGE, VIRGINIA, TO CHARLESTON, WEST VIRGINIA

Natural Bridge to Clifton Forge, Virginia, 40 miles, U.S. 11 and I-64/U.S. 60

Natural Bridge, near the junction of U.S. 11 and State Route 130, is a limestone arch some 215 feet high and 90 feet long, varying in width from 50 to 150 feet. It spans Cedar Creek and supports U.S. 11. A play, "The Drama of Creation," is presented nightly during summer months. Admission is $5; $4 for senior citizens.

Natural Bridge was worshipped by the Monocan Indians as "The Bridge of God." The property where it is located was surveyed by George Washington and was once owned by Thomas Jefferson. It has been called one of the Seven Natural Wonders of the World. There are underground caverns nearby. For information call toll free, 1-800-336-5727 (outside Virginia) or 1-800-533-1410 (in Virginia).

Leave Natural Bridge and follow U.S. Route 11 north, back to Lexington; then turn west on I-64/U.S. 60 toward Clifton Forge. Before us we again see the rolling landscape of the Shenandoah Valley. Now we will cross it from east to west. In some places streams disappear into sinkholes dissolved in the limestone valley floor. Approximately 5 miles east of Clifton Forge we cross (appropriately named) Cowpasture River. Farther north, the Calfpasture and Bullpasture rivers flow into the Cowpasture, which in turn joins the Jackson River about 15 miles south of Clifton Forge, where they then become the James River. The James cuts through a gap in the Blue Ridge east of Natural Bridge and crosses Virginia to flow into the Atlantic Ocean.

Our route now leads out of the Great Valley and across the western folded Ridge and Valley Province, past Clifton Forge and Covington and up the Allegheny Front, which is hardly noticeable here. Between Lexington and Clifton Forge the highway climbs North Mountain to an elevation of more than 2,000 feet and then descends into the synclinal valley between North Mountain and Brush Mountain to the southwest. From the Cowpasture River to Covington on the Jackson River, the route follows approximately the boundary between the central and southern Appalachians. Central Appalachian ridges trend from northeast to southwest. In the southern Appalachians the trend of the ridges becomes more easterly. East of Clifton Forge we can see the gorge of the Jackson River to the south. There is long history of Indian warfare in this area, as indicated by roadside markers. There are a few small farms but for the most part the mountains are heavily wooded.

Appalachia spans thirteen states, but to most people the region's heart is in West Virginia, eastern Kentucky and Tennessee, and southwestern Virginia. Kentucky author Harry Caudill called the area "the least understood and most maligned part of America."

Here you will spot communities with odd names: Meat Camp, Lick Skillet, Nine Times, Lonesome, Hi Hat, Sandy Mush, Meadows of Dan, Beauty, Bitter End, Hell for Certain, and more. You will also see dark, steep, and involuted mountains that look deceptively staid and genteel in the spring when they are covered with redbud, dogwood, and mountain laurel.

Appalachian Culture

You will hear vivid, metaphorical speech. We remember the old man who was rocking on his porch, whittling a whimsical toy called a gee-haw-whimmy-diddle, and think about the creek running by his home. "If that ol' creek didn't rattle, I couldn't go to sleep at night," he said. Or the storekeeper, who observed, as he watched a neighbor trudge up the street, "That feller looks like the hind wheels of hard times."

The area was settled largely in the seventeenth and eighteenth centuries by pioneers from England, Scotland, Ireland, and Germany. The mountains formed a physical and cultural barrier, both isolating and shielding them from change. American geographer Ellen Churchill Semple noted this in 1901 in her article "The Anglo-Saxons of the Kentucky mountains: A study in anthropogeography." More than ninety years ago Semple observed things that are still true to some degree:

> In one of the most progressive and productive countries of the world, and in that section of the country which has had its civilization and its wealth longest, we find a large area where the people are still living the frontier life of the backwoods, where the civilization is that of the eighteenth century, where the people speak the English of Shakespeare's time . . . where money is as scarce as in colonial days. . . . The mountains have caused these conditions to survive, carrying a bit of the eighteenth century intact over into this strongly contrasted twentieth century, and presenting an anachronism all the more marked because [it is] found in the heart of the bustling, money-making, novelty-loving United States.

In the nineteenth century, outsiders began to take interest in the region's great natural wealth—timber and coal. Companies bought the mountaineers' trees, land, and mineral rights cheaply. A pattern of exploitation set in, and the word went out that Appalachian people were slow and not very bright.

One of the authors to describe the mountain mind in a positive way was John Fox Jr. in his turn-of-the-century novel, *The Trail of the Lonesome Pine*. The book told the story of two lovers: Jack Hale, a suave and urbane geologist, out to find his fortune in the undeveloped coal veins of Appalachia, and June Tolliver, a wild, young mountain girl living in the shade of a single, lonesome pine. The trail was the path Jack rode on horseback, back and forth, courting his love. And they grew closer, the citified boy and the country girl, despite feuds and coal-boom pandemonium and the troubles that beset the region when the coal market crumbled. Their drama is re-enacted every summer (June to August) at an outdoor theater in Big Stone Gap. (For reserved seats call 703-523-1235.)

Another way to catch the spirit of Appalachia is to attend one of the music festivals that abound through the area. Information on music festivals can be obtained from Travel West Virginia, State Capitol Complex, Charleston, West Virginia 25303 (telephone toll free 1-800-CALL-WVA). As a mountain proverb says, "God respects you if you work, but loves you if you sing," preferably traditional Scotch-Irish and English ballads, bluegrass and country songs, gospel and shaped-note singing, or folk hymns.

A good spot to sample traditional fare is in small communities. Outside a grocery store one Saturday night we found the store owner's daughter, Beverly, singing haunting mountain tunes and playing her autoharp. The store and the community church are a backroads mecca for all those who love the old-time sounds of a dulcimer, dobro, fiddle, or guitar, as well as buck dancing or flat footing. "That's when you dance like youse a-killin' termites," a local resident explained.

Neighbors up and down the creek come to the "fold" to sit and visit. In the Bible, a fold is a "gathering place," Beverly said. As the sun dropped behind the mountain, fireflies flickered. Like a last fragment of sunlight, a large yellow bird—a meadowlark perhaps—flitted across the newly cut grass and perched on a fence post. "I'm just tryin' to keep alive the music that my parents done," Beverly said.

The fold offers wonderful stuff. But to grapple with the Appalachian core, we must go deeper in West Virginia, through old coal towns in the central and southern part of the state. This is a land of jagged ridges and narrow, winding valleys. The mountains are so vertical they seem concave—which for many years made settlement difficult and travel almost impossible. As Harry Caudill observed, the local residents have been "the least mobile human beings in the country."

How can we describe the people here? A colleague tells of a great storm that left locals snowed in for weeks. A Red Cross team heard about an old lady who lived alone way back in the hills and went to help her. When she appeared at her door, a team worker said, "Hello, we're from the Red Cross." Before he could say another word, she replied, "Well, I don't believe I'm a goin' to be able to help you'uns any this year. It's been a right hard winter."

Appalachian folks are proud, individualistic, and self-reliant. They are also largely poor, uneducated, and easily victimized. Even those who refused to live in the company towns—where the coal bosses held dominion—were profoundly affected by the coal industry and the damage it inflicted on the land and on the mine workers.

The mountain people, as Caudill noted, are also "short-fused." They have their own code of honor—if you are my kinsman or friend, whoever hits you hits me—and a predilection toward fatalism and violence. Counties are still called names like "Bloody Breathitt" (famous for feuding) and "Bloody Harlan" (where the battle over union recognition was more bitter and protracted than anywhere else in the country). All this, plus a much-publicized taste for moonshine, gave the Appalachians a reputation for being ignorant, backward, even barbaric. Historian Arnold Toynbee called them the "Riffs, Albanians, Kurds, Pathans and hairy Ainu" of the New World. Some locals still are battling such stereotypes; others have accepted them.

You will hear mixed views about whether the government helped matters with its "War on Poverty" program, which brought a massive infusion of federal dollars and another layer of bureaucrats. In West Virginia you can see the changes. There are many new buildings in various towns—hospitals, city halls, libraries, vocational–technical schools, community colleges, and several fast-food restaurants—as well as new shopping centers, airports, and stunning interstate highways. The infant mortality rate is down, emigration has been slowed, education is improving, the quality of community services has risen, and the average per capita income is up. However, the new facilities and the wealth are concentrated in population centers. Go a few miles away and you will still see the old poverty, unchanged by all the federal fuss. Some say the new roads have destroyed the old mountain life-style. As Caudill put it, "The Appalachian culture as a living, vibrant thing is dead as a dodo." Others see a resurgence of pride.

A teacher from Left Hand observed: "I think there's a new hillbilly dream: to get a good job away, but then come back and retire in the mountains. Every weekend the highways are full of people returning from Pittsburgh, Wheeling, or other towns to stay home for a few days. There's this joke I hear," he continued. "It's about this man who goes to heaven, and he's looking around up there and sees people chained to a wall. So he asks, 'What's wrong with them?' and St. Peter says, 'Those are hillbillies from West Virginia. If we didn't chain 'em up, they'd go home every weekend.'"

Bernice Smith, a student of Appalachian culture, believes she has seen the growth of a distinct, if subtle, regional culture. "It's in people's style, their manners, their sense of connection to the land and to each other," she said. "When you peel away all the layers and get down to the core, I think it's that here everybody is somebody." Bernice talked about the way people feel held by the mountains, tucked into the tight folds of land.

A few miles away in the tiny settlement of Servia, Steve Taylor was sitting on the porch of a general store selling groceries, supplies, and mountain memorabilia—old hornet's nests, saddlebags, rustic iron tools, political buttons, and mining caps. Steve said that despite the changes that have come to the mountains, people haven't lost their touch with nature or their concern with each other. As the rest of the world becomes increasingly fake and superficial, Appalachia remains a kind of refuge, where people can be exactly who they are without pretense. As Steve spoke, a fellow on another porch across the creek began picking a banjo. The sprightly tune floated down the hillside and up the steep, lush hollow.

Clifton Forge, Virginia, to White Sulphur Springs, West Virginia, 50 miles, I-64

Clifton Forge (population, 5,050) takes its name from an iron smelter that once stood here. A low-grade limonite iron ore was once mined in the area but the mines have been abandoned. Two tall brick smokestacks to the right of the road are the remains of Longdale Furnace, an iron foundry that operated at the south end of Mill Mountain from the late nineteenth to early twentieth century. Had it not been for the railroad, Clifton Forge probably would have been abandoned. It became a division point for the Chesapeake and Ohio Railroad, one of the most important routes serving the eastern coalfields.

It is 19 miles from Clifton Forge to *Covington* (population, 9,060), a town hemmed in on three sides by mountains. Covington was established in 1819, around Fort Young, a frontier post. The town showed little growth until the last part of the nineteenth century when paper, pulp, and chemical plants were established here.

Westward from Covington the route follows the floodplain of Dunlap Creek for about 10 miles and then turns southward for 12 miles, almost parallel to and slowly climbing the Allegheny Front. The route is not steep and it is difficult to determine the boundary between the Ridge and Valley Province and the Plateau. Here the latter is very much dissected and does not have the bold escarpment that forms such a prominent feature farther to the north or south. The state boundary here approximates the boundary of the province, and it may be assumed that when the route enters West Virginia it also enters the Appalachian Plateau.

Our route across West Virginia to Charleston follows an old pioneer wagon road, which followed a still older buffalo trail. Engineers building the roadway through the valleys used shale from the cuts to fill the valleys. These shales contain pyrite, which oxidizes to sulfuric acid, and calcite, which dissolves in acid. This chemical reaction permits the roadbed to compact unevenly and creates bumpy pavement in several places.

THE GREENBRIER

Our next stop is at *White Sulphur Springs* (population, 3,300), site of the Greenbrier, one of the truly great resort hotels in the United States. The springs at the site of the hotel have been a spa since 1778. By the 1830s they were a fashionable rendezvous for the elegant plantation society of the Old South. The Chesapeake and

Ohio Railroad, now CSX Corporation, extended its tracks to White Sulphur Springs in 1868, not long after Union and Confederate troops had fought over the property and each had used it as a hospital. In 1910 the railroad purchased the resort.

In 1942 the Greenbrier was purchased from the C & O Railroad by the U.S. army and turned into a hospital where 20,000 soldiers were treated. The government also confined foreign diplomats from Germany and Japan here. In 1948 the 6,500-acre estate reopened as a luxury hotel and since then has remained a five-star resort. The hotel has 700 rooms and three eighteen-hole golf courses. For many years Sam Snead was the golf pro in residence.

The grand old resort is a throwback to a gentler, nineteenth-century era, when it was a mecca for the Southern aristocracy, and young couples flirted under the watchful eyes of their elders. The Greenbrier is imposing with 6,500 acres of manicured grounds and a lobby so formal that it has its own dress code. Elegant it is, from the carefully preserved Georgian architecture to the formal gardens, where 88,000 tulips bloom amid groves of pink, purple, and white dogwood; lavender and white crab-apple trees; and thousands of rhododendron bushes.

Everything about the resort is on a grand scale. The massive lobbies and public areas abound with statues, oil paintings, prints, elaborately carved wooden trimming, and furniture as old as 150 years. At the height of its April-through-October season, the Greenbrier has 1,500 employees to serve its 1,200 guests. It is a world apart, a place where you dress for dinner and dine in luxurious rooms, softly lit by crystal chandeliers and tiny pink lamps; where cool verandas offer scenic views of the mountains; where waiters arrive within seconds.

For a while, Americans went through a phase of casualness. Now they are returning to elegance. People are coming back to what life once was. In keeping with that, the Greenbrier offers a return to elegance and an opportunity to enjoy dressing up again.

A century ago, the elite of New Orleans and Atlanta society would gather on the oak-dotted lawn of the Greenbrier. There, men sporting top hats and walking sticks mingled with women wearing long, flowing dresses and carrying parasols to enjoy the unlikely combination of champagne and watermelon. Afterward, they would escape the sultry heat, retiring to the cool basement bar for mint juleps.

Today, golf clubs and tennis rackets have replaced walking sticks and parasols; people have abandoned the lawn for the huge swimming pool or one of the myriad tennis courts. But despite the changes through the course of a century, the Greenbrier has retained a sense of elegance as one of America's few five-star resorts. For those requiring a pause between golf and dinner, the Greenbrier still serves tea, accompanied by a musical interlude, promptly at 4:15 every afternoon.

The Greenbrier's original attraction was not golf or tennis. Then, as now, people traveled for hundreds of miles to visit the spas that are fed by the mineral waters of White Sulphur Springs. Guests can soak in large, private tubs filled with mineral water, or relax with a massage.

Legend has it that in 1778 Amanda Anderson, who was hopelessly crippled with rheumatism, was instantly cured after being treated with the spa's famous mineral water. Word spread of the miraculous waters, and the rich and famous flocked to White Sulphur Springs. By 1858, the resort was so popular that a lavish new hotel was built.

The resort has earned not only a national reputation for elegance, but an international following as well. From Andrew Jackson through Dwight D. Eisenhower, heads of state and top-ranking officials from around the world have stayed here. President John Tyler visited with his young bride in 1844; Joseph and Rose Kennedy honeymooned here in 1914; John F. Kennedy visited here as a senator; George Bush visited the Greenbrier when he was Vice President. For more information contact the Greenbrier Hotel, Route 60, White Sulphur Springs, West Virginia 24986 (telephone, 1-800-624-6070; 304-536-1110; Fax 304-536-7834).

White Sulphur Springs to Charleston, West Virginia, 80 miles, U.S. 60 and I-74

Other attractions include the *Greenbrier State Forest* with 5,130 acres for camping, hiking, and swimming, and the Old Stone Church in Lewisburg, the county seat. This was the first Presbyterian Church west of the Allegheny Mountains and has been in continuous use since 1786. *Lewisburg* (population, 3065) dates to 1763 and was first named Big Levels, then Camp Union, and finally Fort Savannah before being chartered as Lewisburg in 1782. It is named for General Andrew Lewis who led forces against the Indians at Point Pleasant in 1774. The area between White Sulphur Springs and Lewisburg is drained by the Greenbrier River which we cross about 5 miles west of White Sulphur Springs. Eight miles south of Lewisburg on State Route 12 is Alderson, the location of the Federal Correctional Institute for Women, where Squeaky Fromme is imprisoned.

We will leave I-64 at a point near Clintonville and continue northwest on U.S. 60, a picturesque winding mountain route that connects places with names like Charmco, Lookout, Hico, and Hawk's Nest. Side roads lead to Clearco, Anjean, Duo, Marfrance, Clifftop, Nallen, and numerous other places with strange-sounding names, usually coal-mining communities. Often these were named for the wives, daughters, or girlfriends of coal company executives. Other times they are a contraction of the company name and sometimes they are named for the executive himself.

If we had continued to follow I-64 we would have passed through Summers County, where the legend of John Henry was born. In the early 1870s when the C & O Railroad built the Big Bend Tunnel at Talcott, a mile of hard, red shale had to be cleared through Big Bend Mountain by driving steel by hand into the hard rock. Reportedly one in every five men was killed as tons of rock crushed them. Legend says John Henry competed against a steam drill in 1873 with a hammer in each hand. He won the race but died in his sleep that night. Others claim he was killed later by a rock blast. When a concrete floor was poured in the tunnel in 1932 the hammer and steel supposedly

New River Gorge Bridge, Fayette County, West Virginia. Photograph courtesy of the West Virginia Division of Tourism and Parks.

HICO

Hico got its name from a brand of chewing tobacco. In 1895 the postmaster moved the post office from his home to a nearby store. The store sold the tobacco called Hico and had a sign outside advertising it. The post office took advantage of the free advertising and adopted the name. Hico sits at the intersection of two scenic highways. I-64/U.S. 60 passes Hico on its 71-mile run from White Sulphur Springs to Gauley Bridge and U.S. 19 passes Hico about halfway along its 45-mile scenic stretch from Bradley to Sutton.

BECKLEY MINE

The Beckley Exhibition Mine has 1,500 feet of underground passages that have been restored in a mine operated by the Phillips family in the late 1800s in what is now part of New River Park. Visitors ride a "man trip" car guided through the mine by veteran miners for an authentic view of low-seam coal mining from its earliest manual stages to modern mechanized operation. The city of Beckley also has restored a three-room house from Sprague, West Virginia. The coal camp and house was once owned by the New River Coal Company, dating back from 1925 through the 1940s. A community of houses was built and owned by the coal company. The working men and their families rented houses according to the size of the family. Coal camps had all the necessities to function through everyday life, such as a company store, company doctors, and churches.

used by John Henry were found in a dirt fill. They had been thrown there after the contest and John Henry's death because superstition prevented anyone from using the hammer again.

Did you know that West Virginia is the only state to have been designated a state by presidential proclamation? It is, so designated by President Abraham Lincoln in 1863. It has an area of 24,282 square miles and a population of about 1.8 million people.

West Virginia has two major topographic regions: the folded parallel ridges of the mountains in the eastern third and a maze of hills and hollows in the dissected plateau to the west. By the time we reach Charmco, some 10 miles west of Clintonville, we are deep in coal-mining country. At Charmco the route makes a 120-degree turn back to the south in the direction of Rainelle and then a ninety-degree turn back to the west.

Coal mining in West Virginia. Photograph courtesy of the West Virginia Division of Tourism and Parks.

Rainelle is a small commercial center, well-known for its sawmills and lumbering. Logs are brought from the surrounding area and the lumber is made into building materials, furniture stock, flooring, and other miscellaneous forms.

The road from Rainelle westward winds near the crest of various ridges of the dissected plateau. The forested uplands are almost unpopulated, in striking contrast to the dense settlements of the valleys. A few fields are devoted to corn, hay, or pasture. From Rainelle it is 18 miles to Hico where we cross U.S. 19, which goes south to Beckley or north to a junction with I-74 northeast of Charleston. Beckley is a coal-mining center, site of the Beckley

HAWK'S NEST STATE PARK

Hawk's Nest State Park encompasses 276 acres bordering a rugged section of the New River Gorge National River. Long known for its panoramic views, the park offers a modern thirty-one-room lodge for overnight guests. Below the lodge the New River forms peaceful Hawk's Nest Lake. Above the lake, the narrow canyon and rushing water create one of the most challenging wild-water boating waters in the nation. An aerial tramway from the lodge serves the lakeside recreational facilities. In the older section of the park is the park's museum. Constructed by the Civilian Conservation Corps in the early 1930s, the rustic museum offers displays of Indian and pioneer artifacts. Admission is free.

Exhibition Coal Mine, the only historically preserved coal mine in West Virginia. The mine was used for the filming of the movie *Matewan*. Retired coal miners guide visitors through 1,500 feet of underground passages.

Beckley (population, 20,500) is also the county seat of Raleigh County in the heart of the New River area. Offering the best white-water rafting in the east, the New River has twenty-six major rapids in one 15-mile stretch. It is thought to be the oldest stream on the North American continent.

U.S. Route 19 south to Beckley crosses New River on the New River Gorge Bridge, the world's largest steel arch bridge. The bridge is the second-highest in the nation and the highest east of the Mississippi River: The top of the roadway is approximately 876 feet above the waters of New River.

Six miles west of Hico we will come to *Hawk's Nest State Park* near Ansted. The Hawk's Nest is a towering rock 585 feet above

View from Hawk's Nest, West Virginia. Photograph courtesy of the West Virginia Division of Tourism and Parks.

New River Gorge. The steep walls of the canyon cut in the horizontal sediments of the plateau are covered with oak, maple, dogwood, and rhododendron. Just downstream, water from New River has been diverted through a 3-mile tunnel to a power plant on the other side of Gauley Mountain. From Hawk's Nest the road descends rapidly to Gauley Bridge, where the Gauley and New rivers join to form the Kanawha River. Our route follows the Kanawha to Charleston. Gauley Bridge was the scene of heavy fighting during the Civil War. In 1860 the old bridge was destroyed during a Confederate retreat. The old bridge piers can still be seen upstream from the present bridge across New River. Gauley Bridge marks the western end of the scenic portion of I-64/U.S. 60. The distance from White Sulphur Springs to Gauley Bridge is 71 miles.

The Kanawha River Valley from Gauley Bridge all the way to its confluence with the Ohio River is well known for its chemical and metallurgical industries, based on local supplies of coal, natural gas, and salt brine. The Kanawha River has a nine-foot channel upstream to the falls at Glen Ferris. Three dams and locks built for this purpose may be seen along the valley. Downstream from Alloy the settled area is almost continuous and we go directly from one town to the next—London, Glasgow, Cedar Grove, Belle, Rand, and Malden—all based on coal and chemicals. Seams of coal may sometimes be seen in the roadcuts. Booker T. Washington, the famous black educator, was born in Malden. A short distance beyond Malden we will see the northern entrance to the West Virginia Turnpike, on the outskirts of Charleston.

CHARLESTON, WEST VIRGINIA

Charleston (population, 59,400) is the capital of West Virginia. The capitol building, on Kanawha Boulevard, faces the Kanawha River. The building, patterned after the U.S. capitol building in Washington, D.C., is the masterpiece of architect Cass Gilbert. The outstanding feature is the rotunda's golden dome, 180 feet above the main floor. It is the largest state capitol dome in the country. From its center hangs a two-ton rock-crystal chandelier, eight feet in diameter. The sliding brass and copper doors on the

Charleston, West Virginia. Photograph courtesy of the West Virginia Division of Tourism and Parks.

WEST VIRGINIA TURNPIKE

The West Virginia Turnpike is a four-lane toll highway, 88 miles in length, between Princeton and Charleston, West Virginia. Interstate 77 is carried by the entire length of the turnpike; Interstate 64 is carried from Charleston to south of Beckley. Described as "an engineering achievement of heroic proportion," the turnpike traverses mountainous terrain that required grades of up to 5 percent and the movement of 70 million cubic yards of earth. The turnpike climbs from an elevation of 600 feet at Charleston to an elevation of 3,400 feet at Flat Top Mountain. The Turnpike has 111 bridges—more than one every mile. Nature's vistas—the view from Flat Top Mountain, the Bluestone Gorge, spring's buds and blossoms, and fall's panoply of color—add aesthetics to the list of conventional values of economy and time found on the turnpike.

north and south sides are decorated with a panel design showing leaves of West Virginia's native trees. This design also adorns the second-floor ceiling. The building's office wings house the state administrative departments, including the Supreme Court and Law Library (open Monday through Saturday, 8:30 to 4:30; 304-348-3809).

The *Capitol Complex* includes the governor's mansion, a cultural center, and several office buildings—all on beautifully manicured lawns and grounds with numerous fountains and historic statues.

The governor's mansion was designed by Walter Martens and constructed in 1924. The mansion is a traditional Georgian colonial structure with a hospitable, homelike, yet dignified air, harmonizing with the other buildings in the complex. The ground floor contains state rooms; the second floor serves as the governor's residence. Tours are conducted on Thursdays and Fridays, 9:30 to 11:30 (304-348-3588).

The *Cultural Center,* described as a "must" for Charleston visitors, houses fine exhibits in the state museum and archives. The West Virginia State Theater within the Cultural Center features a variety of festivals, films, and theatrical productions, all of which are free. The Shop is a craft center that markets literature, recordings, arts, and crafts of West Virginians (open weekdays 9:00 a.m. to 9:00 p.m. and weekends 1:00 p.m. to 9:00 p.m.; 304-348-0220).

Charleston Town Center is adjacent to the Charleston Civic Center Complex. Offering more than 150 shops including four major department stores, this is one of the largest enclosed, inner-city malls in the United States. Its Center Court Atrium features a three-story waterfall and extensive greenery, which is a favorite with visitors and locals alike.

The transformation of Charleston's downtown streets, sidewalks, and facades into an atmosphere of classic urban charm has led to what is becoming known as Charleston's Village District. It includes more than 100 locally owned businesses, including seventy-nine retail stores and twenty-nine restaurants and food emporiums, and numerous important cultural, entertainment, and service organizations. A walk through the streets offers a glimpse of this river city's history. The Charleston Renaissance Corporation furnishes directories of significant historic buildings (304-345-1738). In the eastern end of Charleston are numerous distinctive homes mostly built between 1895 and 1925, in a variety of architectural styles including Greek Revival, Victorian, Queen Anne, Richardsonian Romanesque, Colonial, Georgian, Spanish Colonial, Italianate, and Renaissance. The homes are in a district bordered by Bradford, Quarrier, and Michigan streets and Kanawha Boulevard.

Charleston's Civic Center and Coliseum is a 13,500-seat showplace for concerts or a 12,500-seat arena for basketball. It offers a variety of entertainment year-round as well as a location for meetings, conventions, and trade shows (304-345-1500).

Trolley buses designed as replicas of old-fashioned trolleys shuttle throughout the downtown areas of Charleston providing transportation between the Civic Center, downtown hotels, Charleston Town Center, Downtown Village, the Capitol Complex, and major downtown office buildings (operation, Monday through Saturday, 11:00 a.m. to 7:00 p.m.; the fare is $0.50).

Charleston offers a variety of festivals and events throughout the year. The highlight is the Sternwheel Regatta Festival, an annual river festival that attracts regional and national attention. It is a ten-day event starting the first week in September (Charleston Festival Commission, 304-348-8033).

Charleston, West Virginia, to Pittsburgh, Pennsylvania

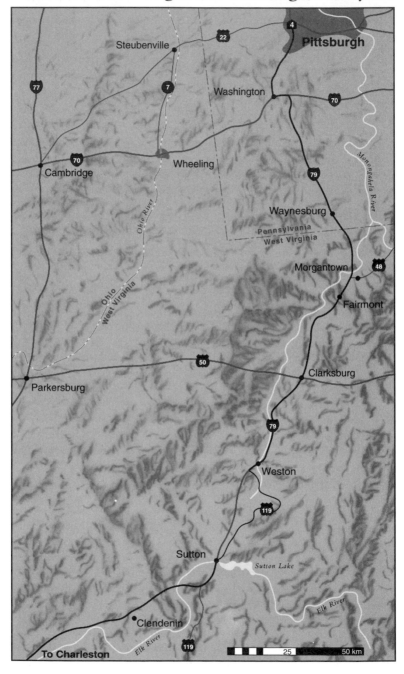

△ Day Three

CHARLESTON, WEST VIRGINIA, TO PITTSBURGH, PENNSYLVANIA

Charleston to Morgantown, West Virginia, 150 miles, I-79

We leave Charleston and head north on Interstate 79—destination, Pittsburgh, Pennsylvania. The entire route, some 227 miles, is mountainous with few cities. State Route 4 and U.S. Routes 19 and 119 tend to parallel the Interstate and serve the smaller communities. Lumbering and mining are the major industries through this region. Most of the hillsides are too steep for the plow or tractor. Numerous crosses along the route evince local religious beliefs.

The many small family graveyards are typical of Appalachia. Family relationships are strong and when someone dies the body is often kept at home until burial. Then burial is in a family plot that can be visited often. Most of the homes in this area are very modest and one wonders why these people settled here in the first place rather than moving on and claiming better land elsewhere. Sometimes the reason was simple—an accident, a horse died, a cart broke down, a young couple could not leave the grave of their only child, fatigue, illness, the lure of the mountains.

Average incomes in this part of West Virginia are low and the unemployment rate is high. The best-paying jobs are usually in the coal mines but since the mines have become mechanized there are not enough jobs to go around. Throughout Appalachia politicians promise more jobs, better roads, and better schools. Road construction is difficult and expensive in the mountains and yet, more and better roads are needed. In some areas students have problems getting to school because of the roads. Valley lands are good and those fortunate enough to have settled in the river valleys have prospered, but the hillside farms are so steep that crops from cultivated hillside farms must be brought down on sleds, and yields are small. This is true throughout much of southern Appalachia. The mule is still an important animal in the mountains. Mules have smaller feet and are more sure-footed than horses and certainly less dangerous than tractors, which turn over on steep hillsides.

The West Virginia motto is "Montani semper liberi." Certainly one of the most mountainous in the country, the state is sometimes called the "little Switzerland" of America. In the modern world the mountaineer must often give up some freedom to survive.

Our route, I-79, is part of the Appalachian highway system. The settlements are in the valleys and there are many mobile homes, which have replaced the traditional mountain cabins. Most of the mountain slopes are forested and the route is scenic. We are deep into coal country but the mines are away from the interstate highway and out of sight. A few scattered oil or gas wells are visible, some pumping, some not. The forests are mixed broad-leaf deciduous and evergreen with most of the evergreens on the sandstone at higher elevations. These add to the attractiveness of the landscape.

Three miles east of Exit 19 is the town of *Clendenin*. Located on the railroad and near U.S. Route 119, Clendenin had the first of the huge chemical plants in the area. Union Carbide Corporation founded the petrochemical industry in 1920 when it purchased a small natural gas plant in Clendenin and transformed it into a combined ethylene and chemicals plant. By 1925 the manufacture of chemicals had grown so that another plant was needed. Expansion continued into the 1940s throughout the region until the Kanawha Valley became known as the Chemical Capital of the World. Clendenin was named for George Clendenin, one of the earliest settlers. Charleston was named for his father, Charles Clendenin.

About 22 miles north of Charleston we see the Light Jordan Baptist Church. Crosses on nearby hills again remind us of the importance of religion in the area. The first Baptist church west of the Allegheny mountains, Simpson Creek Baptist, was organized at Bridgeport, a few miles north of here, in 1774.

Five miles farther along, at a point just south of *Amma,* we see a golf course and signs of tourist development. Most of the people who live in this area work in local mines. At the Servia Rest Area, brochures for tourist attractions include one for the Sutton Lake Recreation Area 12 miles farther up the road. The rest stop has a scenic view of Elk River. As we continue we see a good view of a peneplain just before Exit 57.

Sutton (population, 1,190) (Exit 62) is at the geographical center of West Virginia. It is the county seat of Braxton County and was named for John D. Sutton, its founder. We see sawmills, a few gas and oil wells, and some livestock and dairy farming near Sutton. Signs point to the Oneida and Juliana coal mines.

U.S. Route 119 crosses our Interstate at Exit 99. A short distance to the west is the town of *Weston* (population, 6,000). Weston is a service center for the surrounding area and also has glass industries and several interesting Victorian-era homes. The Weston State Hospital has a main building with nine acres of floor space and is said to be the largest hand-cut stone building in the United States. In recent years Weston has become well-known for its Christmas light displays which include a thirty-nine-minute computerized light show called "Dancing Snowflakes." On the banks of the nearby West Fork River is Jackson's Mill Museum, a reminder of the life of early settlers in the region. The museum is on the grounds of the boyhood home of Stonewall Jackson. Gristmill and water-driven sawmill components, farm tools, weaving equipment, and hand-woven textiles are displayed (open daily 1:00 to 5:00, Memorial Day to Labor Day; admission free; 304-269-5100).

At Nutters Fort, Exit 117, we see another Baptist church. This exit serves as a south exit for *Clarksburg* (population, 21,400). Clarksburg was the birthplace of Stonewall Jackson and the site is marked by a bronze plaque, but he spent most of his boyhood at Jackson's Mill near Weston, 20 miles to the south.

More than 40 percent of the population of Clarksburg is of Italian descent. The West Virginia Italian Heritage Festival held here each Labor Day weekend is a popular event. It is an authentic ethnic Italian celebration featuring food, music, a parade, and cultural activities. (Call 304-622-7314 or write West Virginia Italian Heritage Festival, P.O. Box 1632, Clarksburg, West Virginia 26301.)

Meadowbrook Mall, a large shopping center, is near the second Clarksburg exit where U.S. Route 50 crosses our route going east–west. Twelve miles farther up the road we come to *Fairmont* (population, 22,800). This is the birthplace of Mary Lou Retton, U.S. Olympic gold medalist in gymnastics. The worst mining disaster in West Virginia history occurred just west of Fairmont at Monongah, in 1907, when 361 men lost their lives. Fairmont occupies the steep hills surrounding the Monongahela River, which divides the town into east and west sections. Fairmont was originally two towns, Palatine and Middletown, but was incorporated as Fairmont in 1843. Ferries shuttled people and supplies across the river until a suspension bridge was erected in 1850. Coal is the town's major source of income. Fairmont also manufactures glass, mine machinery, aluminum, and lamps. Pricketts Fort State Park is 2 miles from I-79 Exit 139, just north of Fairmont. Fairmont College, on eighty acres in the city of Fairmont, is a four-year liberal arts college with 6,000 students.

Our route passes just west of *Morgantown* (population, 27,800), home of West Virginia University and the seat of Monongalia County. The university is connected to Morgantown downtown district by a fully automated Personal Rapid Transit System. The computer-controlled system serves as a laboratory for engineering students and urban planners.

Morgantown, West Virginia, to Pittsburgh, Pennsylvania, 60 miles, I-79 and I-279

Six miles farther north we leave West Virginia and enter Pennsylvania. Geologists may notice a change in rock structure starting near the state border. We have been on bedrock of Pennsylvanian age but for about the next 40 miles I-79 crosses Permian bedrock.

These youngest Paleozoic rocks exist only in southwestern Pennsylvania, in the part of the Allegheny Plateau known as the Pittsburgh Plateau. Most of the cuts expose colorfully banded beds containing sequences of grayish sandstones and siltstones, gray to brown to black shales and some coal, light gray limestone, and even redbeds. Geologists think that these formations were laid down in a shallow inland sea that covered this region 290 million to 250 million years ago, at a time when all the world's continents were coming together to form the supercontinent of Pangaea. And then Africa and North America collided, forming the Allegheny Mountains and ending the Permean rock record in this part of the world. The Pennsylvanian-age rocks that contain practically all of the coal mined in this region and throughout Appalachia are beneath the Permean rocks in this area. Still deeper are the Mississippian and Devonian beds that contain the gas that has long been important to the region and especially to Pittsburgh. Some of the reservoirs also contain oil but production has almost ceased. The gas and oil is found at shallow depths of 1,200 to 2,800 feet. Natural gas was one of the most important influences on the industrial revolution that made Pittsburgh into a great steel city.

The moderate relief we see in this part of the Pittsburgh Plateau was created by the small tributaries of the Monongahela River. Fifteen miles into Pennsylvania we come to *Waynesburg* (population, 4,300), named for the Revolutionary War hero, General "Mad" Anthony Wayne. It is the home of Waynesburg College, one of the first colleges in the United States to grant degrees to women. Waynesburg is the seat of Greene County. The Greene County Historical Museum is 3 miles east, via I-79 Exit 3, on State Route 21. The museum is a fifty-two–room mid-Victorian structure with more than half the rooms furnished in period, from the frontier days to the Victorian era (telephone 412-627-3204).

It is 21 miles from Waynesburg to Washington, where Interstate 70 crosses our route. We will continue north on I-79 to Pittsburgh but will come back to I-70 later as we go west to Ohio.

Washington (population, 18,300) is home to Washington and Jefferson College, one of the oldest colleges west of the Allegheny Mountains. The library was a gift from Thomas Jefferson.

Washington also gained fame as a station on the underground railroad during the Civil War and as the home of David Bradford, a leader in the Whiskey Rebellion in 1794. Two miles north in *Arden* is a trolley museum that displays trolleys and standard-gauge railroad equipment.

Bridgeville is at the northern end of the Permean geologic exposure. At the Great Southern Shopping Center turn off I-79 here at Exit 11. At the Old Country Buffet Restaurant, you can get a good lunch at a moderate price. Continuing to Pittsburgh via I-279 and the Fort Pitt Tunnel, we switch from I-79 to I-279 at Exit 15.

As we exit the Fort Pitt Tunnel we get our first view of the Golden Triangle, that point where the Allegheny and Mononga-hela rivers join to form the Ohio River. Scientists tell us that in pre-glacial time three separate major stream systems, the upper, middle, and lower Allegheny, drained western Pennsylvania north-ward to a large northeast-flowing stream in the region of what is now Lakes Erie and Ontario and which probably emptied to the Atlantic Ocean through the Saint Lawrence River. The Ohio was then but a tributary to the Monongahela of the lower Allegheny system. No present-day streams drain the plateau northward. All the rivers united to form the Ohio River system which drains to the Mississippi and on to the Gulf of Mexico.

PITTSBURGH, PENNSYLVANIA

We cross the Monongahela on the Fort Pitt Bridge and enter the Golden Triangle. Point State Park is at the confluence of the three rivers. To the left, across the river, is the Duquesne Incline Rail-way, and to the right, Three Rivers Stadium, where the Pittsburgh Pirates and Steelers play their home games. The river traffic in-cludes numerous pleasure craft and towboats pushing barges. To the left along the south shore of the Monongahela are rail lines with an occasional train entering or leaving the city.

Pittsburgh is a big city, with more than 2.25 million people in the metropolitan area. It reaches up the valleys and hillsides and onto the hilltops of elevation varying from about 700 feet at waters edge to more than 1,200 feet on the plateau at the top. Pittsburgh's

European history dates from the eighteenth-century dispute between the English and the French over claims to the region. The French seized the area from the British in 1754 and built an outpost which they named Fort Duquesne. The British regained the area in 1758 and countered with a fort of their own and called it Fort Pitt for William Pitt, prime minister of England. The settlement that grew around it was called Pittsborough and later Pittsburgh. The site was selected by George Washington, who was then a major in the colonial army.

After the American Revolution Pittsburgh's location on the three rivers made it a major point of departure for settlers headed west. Hundreds of boats and rafts carried pioneers downriver to Ohio, Indiana, Illinois, West Virginia, Kentucky, and other points south and west.

A combination of oil, gas, and cheap coal gave the Pittsburgh area an era of cheap fuel, an era that will neither return nor be duplicated elsewhere. The rivers provided transportation to the coalfields. Not far from Pittsburgh is a layer of coal known as Connellsville coal. Until about 1925 it was the best coking coal in the United States, perhaps in the world, and especially when used under the old-fashioned beehive oven, which was the only device used in this country before 1900. The unusual excellence of this coke for making iron gave Pittsburgh an advantage over all other iron centers, and since limestone and iron ores occur nearby it is easy to see why this city became the greatest iron-manufacturing city in the world.

To appreciate present-day Pittsburgh one needs to know something of its past. J. Russell Smith wrote in 1925 that "Pittsburgh . . . is a land of fire. . . . miles of coalcars, of burning coke-ovens, smoke, dust, sweat, black hillsides, colleries, mine conveyors, railroad tracks, blackened steel plants, flaming furnaces, white-hot metal pouring, red-hot metal cooling, heavy rolls, pressing red-hot plates with roaring noise, shears cutting the plates into pieces, giant cranes lifting and dropping them with a clang."

Pittsburgh remained a smokey city until after World War II, but today it is a far cry from the old smokey city Smith described. As the steel industry in the United States declined, Pittsburgh officials took advantage of the opportunity to pass strict smoke-control laws and as a result Pittsburgh now has clean air. Educational, recreational, and cultural aspects are now as important as commerce and manufacturing. The factories that once crowded the riverbanks and the point have been replaced by new buildings and parks.

Nowhere is this more apparent than in the *Strip* district, the city's wholesale and retail distribution point where you can buy produce, flowers, and meat fresh off a truck. The Spaghetti Warehouse, a 100-year-old warehouse at Twenty-sixth and Smallman streets, was transformed into an Italian restaurant complete with a trolley-car dining room. A few blocks away an appliance warehouse was converted into the Metropol, a nightclub. A warehouse for plants is now La Prima Espresso Company (205 Twenty-first Street). On Seventh and Penn streets you will find the Stanley Theater restored to its original splendor.

Today Pittsburgh's source of prosperity comes not from metals but from minds. Thousands of jobs have been added in medicine, biotechnology research, information, and financial services. With more than fifty-five hospitals and thirty-one colleges in the area, including six hospitals affiliated with the University of Pittsburgh, the city is now known as a transplant and medical research center, and Carnegie Mellon University is a leading center for computer science, robotics, and artificial intelligence. With universities and research centers as its leading employers, the city's leading export is now knowledge, not steel.

Pittsburgh's streets have no consistent geometric pattern. Starting from the Point, the main thoroughfares tend to parallel the rivers and the cross streets are at right angles to them, but farther out they follow the contours of the hills.

Pittsburgh's City Planning Commission recognizes eighty-eight neighborhoods in the city. These areas were established as immigrants arrived to work in the mills or to establish businesses. Most of the groups are now scattered but the people still like the idea of neighborhoods and because the neighborhood identities have remained strong (a feature that has died out in most large cities), the neighborhood tavern thrives here. And there is a great variety of ethnic restaurants.

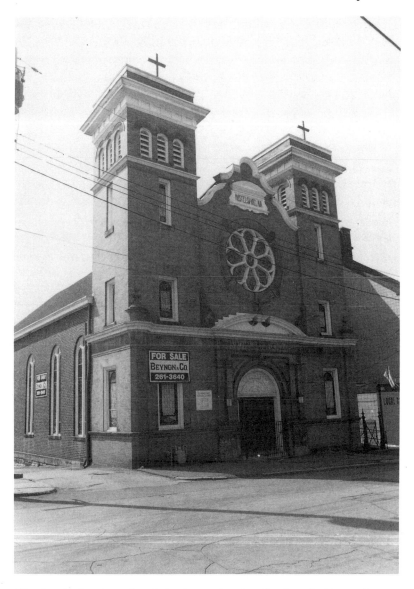

The last Bohemian church in Pennsylvania, Pittsburgh, Pennsylvania.
Photograph by P. P. Karan.

The *Fort Pitt Blockhouse,* built in 1764, is all that remains of the original Fort Pitt; but a museum within the park focuses on the early history of western Pennsylvania. The museum is a replica of one of the original parts of the old fort (admission: adults $1.50; senior citizens $1.00; call 412-281-9284 for additional information). A focal point in the park is a computerized white- and gold-lighted fountain that sprays water to heights of 150 feet.

Across the Monongahela, not far from the Fort Pitt Bridge, the Duquesne Incline and the Monongahela Incline climb 793 feet to the top of *Mount Washington,* where several restaurants have panoramic views of the Golden Triangle. From the top , you can see the Allegheny and the Monongahela rivers join to form the Ohio River. Under a setting sun during the summertime this is a river of gold. From here you can also see star-shaped Fort Duquesne. The lower station is at 1197 West Carson Street, the main street paralleling the river on the south side. At the top the trip ends at 1220 Grandview Avenue. (One-way fare is $1.00; for information, call 412-381-1665 for the Duquesne Incline or 412-231-5707 for the Monongahela Incline.)

Much of Pittsburgh's history is captured in the city's wealth of landmark architecture and historic residential districts. Highlights include the sumptuously restored Pittsburgh and Lake Erie Railroad Station at *Station Square* (now the centerpiece of a lively office, restaurant, shopping, and entertainment complex) and the Beaux-Arts and neo-classical structures crowding the Oakland section. For information on tours and attractions, call the Pittsburgh Historical and Landmarks Foundation (412-471-5808).

Pittsburgh is home to the four-time Super Bowl champions, the Pittsburgh Steelers, and to the Penguins hockey team, as well as to the Pirates, who play at Three Rivers Stadium. Additional information about Pittsburgh can be obtained from the Greater Pittsburgh Convention and Visitors Bureau, 4 Gateway Center, Pittsburgh, Pennsylvania (telephone 1-800-821-1888).

The *Gateway Clipper Fleet,* operating from a dock near Station Square at the south end of Smithfield Bridge over the Monongahela, offers scenic cruises on the rivers. (Narrated sightseeing cruises cost $7.50 for a two- to two-and-one-half-hour trip; senior citizens, $6.25; call 412-355-7979 for information.)

The *Golden Triangle* has the best downtown shopping, with major department stores, specialty and high-fashion shops. Pittsburgh Plate Glass (PPG) Place at Market Square offers shopping and noontime concerts in summer.

Fifth Avenue, one of the main routes east from the Golden Triangle, passes through the *University of Pittsburgh* campus. On the right side just beyond Bigelow Boulevard is the Cathedral of Learning, a forty-two-story Gothic stone tower. This is the tallest tower on a campus in the United States. Just behind the tower is the Heinz Memorial Chapel, a French Gothic interdenominational chapel with a marble altar, carved woodwork, and seventy-five-foot stained glass windows. (For special programs, concerts, recitals, and tours, call 412-624-4157).

The Greater Pittsburgh Convention and Visitors Bureau's Visitor Information Center is at 4 Gateway Center (412-281-9222), and in the Mount Washington Center in the Grandview Avenue Branch of the Carnegie Library (412-381-5134). Both centers provide brochures for self-guided tours. Gray Line offers three different bus tours, April through October (412-741-2720).

Pittsburgh, Pennsylvania, to Cleveland, Ohio

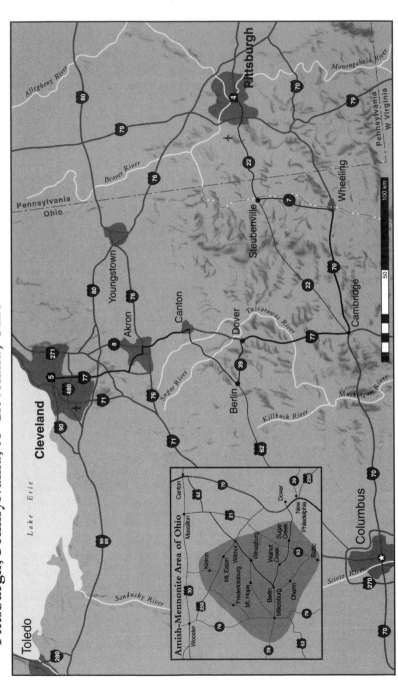

△ Day Four

PITTSBURGH, PENNSYLVANIA, TO CLEVELAND, OHIO

Pittsburgh, Pennsylvania, to Cambridge, Ohio, 55 miles, I-79, I-70, I-77

We travel to Cleveland, Ohio, by way of Wheeling, West Virginia; and Cambridge, Berlin, Canton, and Akron, Ohio. We will go back across the Fort Pitt Bridge, through the Fort Pitt Tunnel, and take I-279 to I-79 back to Washington, Pennsylvania. There we will turn west on I-70. It is about 15 miles to the West Virginia Welcome Station, and another 10 miles to Wheeling where we will again cross the Ohio River.

Wheeling (population, 42,100) is a river city. In fact, part of it is on an island. Wheeling was the site of the last battle of the American Revolution, 11 to 13 September 1782. A historical marker on Main Street marks the site of the old Fort Henry. Wheeling was the first capital of West Virginia. The suspension bridge over the Ohio at Wheeling, built in 1847 to 1849, is 900 feet long, one of the world's longest spans over a river. At the time of its construction it was the longest single span in the world. West Virginia Independence Hall at Sixteenth and Market streets was formerly the Wheeling Custom House. Built in 1859, it was the location of the convention that declared West Virginia's independence from Virginia. The building has been restored and houses historical exhibits (304-233-1333).

The Island, Wheeling, West Virginia. Photograph courtesy of the West Virginia Division of Tourism and Parks.

Wheeling is the seat of Ohio County and was settled in 1769. In the early part of this century it had a thriving steel industry but it has declined. Wheeling's manufacturing industries now include sheet metal, tin containers, paints, axes, tools, tobacco products, and meat packing. A radio station, WWVA, is nationally famous for its weekly broadcasts of country music from a former movie theater on Main Street. "It's that Wheeling Feeling. Live from Capitol Music Hall, Wheeling, West Virginia, it's Jamboree USA!" That's how the master of ceremonies opens the popular Saturday-night show. Fans wander to the backstage door, eager to talk to

Southern Ohio farm, near Cambridge. Photograph by P. P. Karan.

their favorite stars; mothers walk up and down aisles carrying babies; teenagers and grandmothers race down front to snap pictures of people like Charlie Rich, Johnny Cash, and Loretta Lynn. To the people of the upper Ohio Valley, country music "tells it like it is," and they like it.

From Wheeling we continue west on I-70 to Ohio, just across the river. The welcome station has some brochures. From here it is approximately 45 miles to Cambridge, where we turn north on I-77.

Between Wheeling and Cambridge, strip mining is much in evidence. At St. Clairsville there is a large shopping center near the highway. Some of the strip mined areas have been restored and seeded in grass for pasture for cattle and sheep. This is primarily an agricultural area with small service centers every few miles.

Cambridge (population, 12,900) is famous for its glassworks, but like the steel mills in Pittsburgh and Wheeling, most are now inactive. Only one glass blower is still in business and this is a small operation. Three museums display Cambridge glassware. The Cambridge Glass Museum at 812 Jefferson Avenue displays more than 5,000 pieces of Cambridge glass as well as Cambridge Art Pottery (614-432-3045). The Degenhart Paperweight and Glass Museum, Highland Hills Road at U.S. Route 22 and I-77, has a gift shop and video program (614-432-2626). The National Cambridge Collectors Museum of Cambridge Glass just east of I-77 on U.S. Route 40 displays glass made by the Cambridge Glass Company (614-432-4245). The Cambridge Glass Company was chartered in 1873 and operated until 1958. During these years the company operated its own coal mines and gas wells. In the 1920s and 1930s the company had 700 employees and worked three shifts a day.

Dover to Canton, Ohio, 56 miles, I-77, Hwy. 39

THE AMISH

We leave Cambridge and head north on I-77. At Dover we turn west on State Route 39. We are now in *Amish country,* one of the highlights of the trip. This area of Ohio has the world's largest community of Amish. The first settlement we see is Sugarcreek, known as "Little Switzerland of Ohio," because of its unique Swiss-style architecture. Amish and Mennonites are usually found in proximity and have made a distinctive impact on the landscape. In part the coexistence of Amish and Mennonites is because many Amish have rebelled against the rigid discipline, severe restrictions, and spartan life-style of their community, and have turned to the similar but less restrictive Mennonite congregations, which thus have grown up near the Amish. Consequently, it is difficult to separate the cultural landscape of Amish and Mennonites, not only because of cultural similarity, but also because neither group forms a completely homogeneous settlement. Amish, Mennonites, and "English" farmers are always intermixed.

The Amish and Mennonites share a common cultural and strongly religious heritage, and many aspects or facets of their life are identical, or at least quite similar. For example, both employ dress restrictions, and frequently have similar-appearing farmsteads. Hence Amish and Mennonites are often confused with one another. The Mennonites are a product of the Anabaptist movement led in the sixteenth century by Menno Simons, a Dutch reformer-priest. They migrated to North America from southern Germany and northern Switzerland in the eighteenth century. As a result they are sometimes called the Swiss Brethren. The Amish are a splinter group of the Swiss Brethren, founded by Jacob Amman in the late seventeenth century. Because they believed the Mennonites and other Protestant reformers had not gone far enough in purifying the Christian church, the Amish have been aptly characterized as the "reformers of the Reformation." Although some Amish came to the United States in the eighteenth century, most migrants arrived between 1815 and 1840.

The Amish–Mennonite landscape here is one in which religious ideas account for a large number of the components. You will notice the distinctive Amish barn, farmyard, and house. Because electrical power is forbidden or restricted, you will see windmills on true Amish farms. Houses and barns rarely have lightning rods, since these are considered by the Amish to be "against God's will." However, we will find electricity on properties owned by Amish tenants. The Amish construct Sweitzer barns of the type built in southern Germany or Switzerland, the area from which the group migrated between 1815 and 1860. Traditional practices such as stacking straw from threshold grain outside the barnyard or the shocking of corn in the fall are maintained.

Most Amish farmyards have at least one kitchen garden placed conspicuously in front of or by the side of the house. A larger "truck patch" containing potatoes, sweet corn, and other vegetables is also found, but its location is not as conspicuous as that of the kitchen garden, which is often surrounded by a whitewashed board fence. Whitewashing is equated among the Amish with cleanliness and order; the fences, house, and other smaller buildings are painted annually.

Amish homes are large to accommodate big families as well as to house the church services that each farmer is expected to host period-

Amish country, Berlin, Ohio. Photograph by P. P. Karan.

ically. The most common house type is the four-over-four house. Many farmsteads have two houses, often connected by a closed passageway. The second house is generally for grandparents. Sometimes instead of building a separate house, the existing dwelling is enlarged to include a set of rooms for the older generation.

The Amish depend on horse-drawn buggies for transportation, so the small-town service centers, stores, and public facilities provide hitching rails. Since the Amish react adversely to formal education, which might weaken their community, settlements maintain small, private schools for Amish children only.

Two markets have developed in the Amish area of Ohio. One is designed to provide services to the Amish such as those associated with horse-drawn transportation—blacksmiths, harness makers, and buggy works. Also stores sell kerosene heaters and lamps, charcoal irons, hand tools and implements, pottery crocks, gray and blue enamelware utensils, plain black shoes, and simple clothing.

The other is related to commercial tourism, which is designed to exploit the picturesque life-style of the Amish countryside. Many households take advantage of visitors to sell foodstuffs produced on the farm or made at home. Markets often sell "Amish foods" and Amish restaurants proliferate. A rural restaurant near Berlin even advertises an "Amish salad bar." Tourist industries produce furniture, clocks, quilts, and dolls, using traditional designs and colors.

Der Dutchman of Walnut Creek claims to be the original Amish restaurant. The restaurant offers a picturesque view of the Genza Bottom, a beautiful Amish farming valley. Continue west on State Route 39 to the junction of U.S. 62 at Berlin, where you can visit the Amish Heritage Village on Route 39 (for information call 216-893-2951).

Turn back northeast in the direction of Canton. We will be in Amish country for about 15 miles. Just south of Massillon, U.S. 62 joins U.S. 30 and continues to the east, where it intersects I-77 at the south edge of Canton. Here, turn north on I-77.

Canton to Cleveland, Ohio, 30 miles, I-77

Canton (population 89,100) was the home of President William McKinley (twenty-fifth President). The McKinley National Memorial, a 23-acre national landmark is next to Monument Park, at Seventh Street, N.W. The McKinley Museum of History, Science, and Industry is next to the park, north of Seventh Street (216-455-7043). Canton also has the Pro Football Hall of Fame at 2121 George Halas Drive, N.W. The hall has films, memorabilia, and a research library. The Canton Classic Car Museum with antique classic and special interest cars is at Marker Avenue, 0.5 mile east of the Tuscarawas Street exit from I-77 (216-455-3603).

Canton is an industrial city at the southern edge of a great industrial megalopolis that includes Akron, Cleveland, Sandusky, and Toledo in Ohio and Detroit in Michigan. All of these cities

Firestone Plant, Akron, Ohio. Photograph by P. P. Karan.

have suffered in recent years as our economy has shifted from industry to a service-oriented post-industrial economy.

It is roughly 20 miles from Canton to *Akron* (population, 226,900), once the tire-making center of the world. Now most of the tires are made elsewhere, many of them in Mexico. Akron is still the corporate headquarters for Goodyear, Goodrich, Firestone, Bridgestone, General, and Uniroyal and the city now has many high-tech industries, including the Firestone and Goodyear laboratories for research in rubber and plastics. Space suits worn by the first U.S. astronauts were made at B.F. Goodrich. The University of Akron's Institute of Polymer Science is well-known for its research.

Akron is also a great merchandising center and was once well-known for the manufacturing of breakfast cereals. The old mills and grain silos of the original Quaker Oats Company at Quaker Square, 120 East Mill Street, are now occupied by the Akron

Hilton Inn, five restaurants, a shopping mall, and a model railroad museum.

Akron has a great variety of cultural and sporting activities, eleven metropolitan parks, and numerous shopping complexes. The World Series of Golf is held on the Firestone course in August each year. The All-American Soapbox Derby is held in Akron and the Firestone Tournament of Bowling Champions is held here in April each year. Goodyear World of Rubber at 1201 East Market Street is a museum depicting the history of rubber. Admission is free (216-796-2044). Stan Hymet Hall, 714 North Portage Path, is a sixty-five-room mansion built in 1911 to 1915 by Frank A. Seiberling, founder of Goodyear and Seiberling Rubber Companies. It is considered one of the finest examples of Tudor Revival architecture in the United States. The house contains original antique furniture and art treasures and has a Japanese garden (216-836-9075).

After leaving Akron, continue north on I-77 to Cleveland.

CLEVELAND, OHIO

Cleveland, like Pittsburgh, is a big city with nearly 2 million people in the metropolitan area. An industrial giant on Lake Erie, it is part of the Great Lakes manufacturing megalopolis. It ranks among the ten largest manufacturing cities in the United States. John D. Rockefeller founded the Standard Oil Company here in 1870 and made Cleveland the oil center of the nation. The company, now BP America/The Standard Oil Company of Ohio, has its world headquarters in Public Square. Cleveland is at the mouth of the Cuyahoga River, the northern end of the Ohio and Erie Canal. The completion of the canal in 1832 brought a wave of immigrants to Cleveland and it was their labor that built Cleveland into an industrial giant, where fortunes were made in shipments of coal, limestone, and iron ore, in manufacturing of steel and iron, and in oil, railroads, and heavy equipment. Although many of these industries have declined, Cleveland is still home to more than thirty major manufacturing corporations and many smaller ones.

It's relatively easy to get around in Cleveland. The city sits in a "V" or "Y" formed by I-80 and I-90, two major transcontinental routes. I-90 goes through the heart of the city and then east along the lakeshore. I-80 carries traffic from the southern suburbs eastward to Warren, Niles, and Youngstown. On the west side of Cleveland these routes converge on the Ohio Turnpike at Elyria. Downtown Cleveland is the northern terminus of I-71 and I-77 which brings traffic from the south and southwest. I-271 and I-480 bypass the city.

Cleveland's streets are in a grid pattern that centers on *Public Square*. Euclid Avenue is the major business thoroughfare. It leads from the square to the eastern suburbs. Ontario Avenue runs north–south through the square. It divides the city into east and west.

As we approach *North Coast Harbor* the Coast Guard Station is on the right. The USS *Cod,* a World War II submarine, is here. It is open to visitors daily 10:00 a.m. to 5:00 p.m. 1 May to Labor Day (admission: adults $4, senior citizens $2; 216-566-8770).

Just beyond the Coast Guard Station on the right the lake steamer *Mather* is docked. It was an ore carrier, named for Sam Mather, a steel and shipping magnate. At the end of the pier we see the *Goodtime III,* a 1,000-passenger cruise ship, which offers river and lake cruises (216-861-5110). Many other ships visit Cleveland during the summer, offering tours (216-621-4110). To the west of the harbor a couple of hundred yards away we see the Cleveland Stadium, home of the Cleveland Indians and Cleveland Browns.

The influence of the prominent few who shaped Cleveland a century ago is still very much in evidence, from the grand homes that line the streets of Shaker Heights to the downtown buildings that have become landmarks. Initial plans for downtown, for instance, were conceived by the prominent urban planner and architect Daniel H. Burnham in 1903. More recently the city has initiated a Civic Vision 2000 Plan which includes many development projects in downtown.

A more interesting development is the success of new establishments in *the Flats,* along the banks of the Cuyahoga River where it meets the lake. Nightclubs, restaurants, and a few residential lofts aimed primarily at upwardly mobile, young white-collar workers are thriving; within sight, downstream, are the mills, factories, and warehouses that first laid claim to the river and to the city.

The self-guided walking tour prepared by the Convention and Visitors Bureau (1-800-321-1001) includes the Federal Reserve Bank (1455 East Sixth Street, telephone 216-579-2000). Opened in 1923 and designed by Cleveland architects Walter and Weeks in pink Siena marble, the bank's interior lobby is spectacular. Also of note is the Western Reserve Building (1468 West Ninth Street), designed by Daniel H. Burnham and completed in 1888; and the seventeen-floor Rockefeller Building (614 Superior Street, N.W.), opened in 1905 as the city's first skyscraper.

Every tour of Cleveland must include a trip up to the observation deck of the fifty-two-story Terminal Tower in Public Square (telephone 216-621-7981). The city's tallest building, it was built as a railroad passenger terminal in 1927 to 1930. Also not to be missed is a walk through the century-old, glass-covered Arcade (401 Euclid Avenue), which was the city's first shopping center and is the largest such arcade in the country.

Museums and galleries of world renown surround *Case Western Reserve University:* The Cleveland Museum of Arts (11150 East Boulevard; telephone, 216-421-7340), which exhibits an extensive collection of European, Asian, African, Indian, American, ancient Roman, and Egyptian art; the Cleveland Museum of Natural History, Wade Oval, University Circle; and the Cleveland Health Education Museum, 8911 Euclid. The Western Reserve Historical Society, 10825 East Boulevard, maintains an auto-aviation museum as well as a historical museum and library. Up Murray Hill Road toward Cleveland Heights and Shaker Heights, the Little Italy neighborhood has become home to artists' studios and galleries, large and small. The Murray Hill Market sells crafts (2181 Murray Hill Road; telephone, 216-791-9679).

Cleveland has more than 19,000 acres of parkland in twelve reservations, their connecting parkways, and Cleveland Metroparks Zoo. More than 100 miles of parkways provide access to a great variety of facilities. The parks also provide wildlife sanctuaries and wildlife-management areas. The Rocky River Reservation is the largest, with more than 3,400 acres. It includes the valley of Rocky River, winding its way north to Lake Erie. Massive shale cliffs along the river rise above the willows, sycamores, and cottonwoods. Wildlife

LTV Steel Plant, Cleveland, Ohio. Photograph by P. P. Karan.

Mill workers' houses, older section of Cleveland, Ohio. Photograph by P. P. Karan.

is common and visitors can expect to see numerous bird species and some common Ohio mammals, including the white-tailed deer. Rocky River Valley was settled early in this area's history and reflects many of the sights common to the first settlers. Frostville Museum, an affiliate of Cleveland Metroparks, illustrates how the nineteenth-century settlers lived and worked in the valley. Emerald Necklace Marina is an authorized lease-operated marina located in Scenic River Park of Rocky River Reservation. It offers boat docking, storage facilities, launching facilities with easy access to Lake Erie, food, fishing tackle, bait, and boating accessories (216-226-3030).

Immigrants brought their food preferences with them and just about every kind of ethnic cuisine can be found. The city is one of the most heterogeneous in the nation. More than half the population is either foreign-born or of the second generation. No single nationality dominates. The British and Czechs have the most, closely followed by the Germans. The Poles, Italians, Yugoslavs, Hungarians, and Russians are all well represented. The Cultural Gardens of Cleveland are unique. The idea behind them is to harmonize the different foreign groups, rather than melt them down. The city gave space to each cultural group with the understanding that each group would establish a memorial to someone from their native land that symbolized the culture of that country. A German garden was planned as a shrine to Mendelssohn, the English to Shakespeare, the Italians to Virgil, and the Hungarians to Liszt. The Czechs and Slovaks have separate areas.

The people of Cleveland are very civic-minded. They have a fine civic center and symphony orchestra. The idea of a community chest originated in Cleveland in 1913. But it is heavy industry that made the money and for which Cleveland is best known. Perhaps the principal reason for Cleveland's development as an industrial city is that it is in a direct line from the Mesabi Range to the Pennsylvania coalfields, and it is on Lake Erie. But Cleveland, like many other post-industrial cities, is changing from heavy industry to postmodern high-tech industries, although much heavy industry remains. As we leave Cleveland on U.S. Route 6 by way of Clifton Avenue, we pass through a variety of neighborhoods, ranging from working class to luxury.

Cleveland, Ohio, to Detroit, Michigan

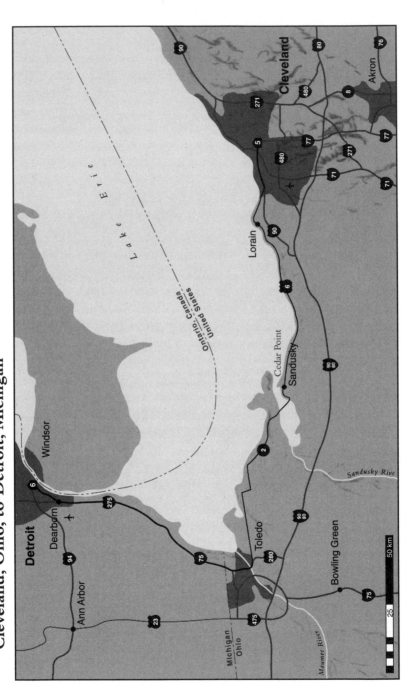

△ Day Five

CLEVELAND, OHIO, TO DETROIT, MICHIGAN

Proceed west from Cleveland along Lake Erie toward Sandusky. As we approach *Loraine* (population, 75,500) we see vineyards, as well as corn, soybeans, pasture, and small orchards. We are approaching one of Ohio's wine-producing regions. Loraine is on the lakeshore and is a site of heavy industry. Loraine lends its name to large earth-moving and road-building machinery.

Sandusky to Toledo, Ohio, 70 miles, Hwy. 6 and 2

The Ohio Wine Producers Association has forty-two wineries, twenty-two of them in the Lake Erie district. Some dozen or so of these are clustered near *Sandusky* (population, 30,600). Some of the grapes are grown on islands in Lake Erie. From Loraine Lake View Park, a city park on the lakeshore, we get a good view of the lake with its variety of boats. As we continue west near Vermillion we see more boats and a variety of tourist facilities. Vermillion takes its name from the red clay found in the area that is used for tinting paint.

Northeast of Sandusky, *Cedar Point* extends into Lake Erie. There is a large family-type amusement park and resort on the point offering summer jobs for many college students, and entertainment for all. The 120-year-old resort is the nation's largest ride park. It has more than fifty rides, including ten roller coasters, miles of midway, and five theaters (419-626-0830).

Southeast of Sandusky on U.S. 250 just north of the Ohio Turnpike Exit 7 is Lake Erie Factory Outlet Center, Ohio's largest outlet center. Nearby is Sandusky Mall. Each has a great variety of stores.

Sandusky was settled in 1816 at a natural harbor formed by Cedar Point and Marblehead Peninsula. It is one of the largest coal-shipping ports on the Great Lakes. Its lakeside resorts and access to Lake Erie make it a popular summer vacation spot. On nearby Marblehead Peninsula, a resort called Lakeside has some of the largest summer conference facilities in the Middle West. It has one of the few remaining Chautaquas in the country. Nationally known performers are featured through the season.

Firelands Wind Cooperative, at 917 Bardshar Road, Sandusky, serves as a central processing plant for four wineries. The original wine cellars and home constructed by the Mantey family in 1880 serves as today's centerpiece for Firelands. The Firelands portion of Connecticut's Western Reserve was allotted to citizens whose homes had been burned by the British during the Revolutionary War, but the area was not settled until the 1800s. Edward Mantey, who established Mantey Vineyards, was one of the early settlers. Over the years new varieties of grapes have been planted, more vineyards cultivated, and modern processing equipment employed alongside traditional old-world winemaking methods to produce some of the finest wines in the eastern United States. The microclimate of the area is ideal for grape growing. Lake Erie's temperate breezes allow for a longer growing season, permitting cultivation of a wide variety of grapes, from the traditional Catawba and Concord varieties to the classic Cabernet and Chardonnay. Firelands wines have received increasing acclaim at national and international competitions. The tour of the winery includes observation of the wine cellar, bottling line, and champagne room from an elevated walkway, a multi-media presentation, and a sample of Firelands's award-winning wines and grape juice. The gift shop has wines, cheese, and fresh-baked bread (419-625-5474 or 1-800-548-WINE).

Several shipping companies offer Lake Erie cruises. The Sandusky Boat Line offers a full-day excursion on the M/V *City of Sandusky* to the historic Kelley's Island, Middle Bass Island, and Put-in-Bay, with time to sightsee at each stop (419-627-0198). The Goodtime Island Cruises, Inc., offer one-day cruises (419-625-9692). Several ferry boats carry passengers to the islands. Put-in-Bay Line Company's *Jet Express* is advertised as the fastest way to Put-in-Bay (1-800-245-1JET).

Put-in-Bay got its name because it provided excellent refuge in its protected harbor. It is on South Bass Island and is known for its wineries, caves, and fish hatcheries, as well as its tourist facilities. A monument to Commodore Oliver Hazard Perry is just outside town. When Perry defeated the British fleet in the Battle of Lake Erie (1812) it was the only time in history that an entire British fleet had been defeated.

Vacationers flock to South Bass Island for many reasons, but Put-in-Bay is probably foremost. Put-in-Bay is where the action is—where they will find excitement, plenty of shops, good food, and fun. If you want to rock the night away at one of the area's hot spots or relax on a beach, you won't be disappointed. What began as a wine-producing island evolved into a resort.

Port Clinton, just across the bay from Sandusky, on Route 2, is also a tourist center. It has a variety of excellent facilities and is the key port for fishermen. Just west of Port Clinton is Camp Perry, where the National Rifle and Pistol Matches have been held continuously, except for a few war years, since 1907. The country's finest marksmen gather for approximately thirty days during midsummer to compete for trophies and national titles.

DAVIS-BESSE NUCLEAR POWER STATION

Navarre Marsh is the site of the *Davis-Besse Nuclear Power Station.* The power station is jointly owned by Toledo Edison and the Cleveland Electric Illuminating Company. Toledo Edison operates the Nuclear Power Station. About one half of the power (7,700,000 megawatt hours) generated at Davis-Besse is provided to Toledo Edison's integrated electrical network for distribution in northwest Ohio. The Cleveland Electric Illuminating Company receives the other half of the power output, providing electricity to Cleveland and to northeast Ohio.

The decision to build the Davis-Besse Nuclear Power Station was made in 1968 after years of intensive studies on population growth, industrial expansion, cost of traditional power plants, and their effect on the environment. The power station is located on a 954-acre site in the Navarre Marsh, a wildlife refuge. Toledo Edison and the U.S. Fish and Wildlife Service cooperate to maintain a satisfactory water level in the marsh to sustain a habitat for wildlife.

Davis-Besse is considered to be one of the most efficient nuclear power-plants in the world, and definitely one of the top ten in the United States. About half a penny's worth of uranium generates one kilowatt hour of electricity at Davis-Besse, the same amount of electrical energy that two cents' worth of coal produces at Toledo Edison's fossil-fueled plants, or as much as fourteen cents for oil-fired energy generation.

One of the major problems facing nuclear-power stations is the disposal of radioactive waste material. All spent fuel used by Davis-Besse is stored on site in a spent-fuel pool until the federal government develops one national storage facility for all high-level waste. All low-level radioactive waste—such as protective clothing—used in the station is currently shipped to Barnwell, South Carolina. However, this facility will close at the end of 1992. All waste must then be stored on site until Midwest Compact, which Ohio belongs to, opens a storage facility. This will probably not occur until 1995, at the earliest. Davis-Besse has the on-site capacity to store about five years' worth of low-level radioactive waste. For information and a tour of the Davis-Besse Nuclear Power Station, contact Davis-Besse Site Tour Coordinator, Edison Plaza, 300 Madison Avenue, Toledo, Ohio 43652 (telephone, 419-321-7145).

TOLEDO, OHIO

A few miles west of Davis-Besse is *Toledo* (population, 343,900), a great industrial center and one of the busiest freshwater ports in the world. For a tour of the port contact the Toledo–Lucas Port

Authority, One Maritime Plaza, Toledo, Ohio 43604 (telephone 419-243-8251).

Toledo's importance stems from its location at the mouth of the Maumee River, the largest river flowing into the Great Lakes. Toledo's harbor has 35 miles of frontage. Pipelines for crude oil and gas terminate here and Toledo is a major refining center and a large producer of glass. Toledo is also a major rail center. The Erie and Kalamazoo Railroad, completed in 1836, was the first railroad west of the Allegheny Mountains, and it started in Toledo.

Toledo occupies the site of an old fort, *Fort Industry,* built in 1794. It stood near the present Summit and Monroe streets. A boundary dispute with Michigan in 1835 gave Toledo to Ohio and Michigan gained its upper peninsula as compensation.

Toledo has a large Metropark system with each park preserving some quality native to the area. Promenade Park along the Maumee River is a good location for viewing freighters and towboats on the river. A lake steamer, the *Wallis B. Boyer,* is docked at International Park, across from Portside. The *Boyer* was launched in 1911 and retired in 1980. In its day it was the largest and most modern ship on the Great Lakes. It has been refurbished and is open to visitors (admission: adults $3.50, over 62 or under 12 $2.50; 419-698-8252).

The highly respected University of Toledo was established in 1872. Guided tours are available by appointment (419-537-2696). An interesting shopping area is the Portside Festival Market Place, a complex of specialty shops on the waterfront. Toledo also has four large shopping malls with a great variety of department stores and shops.

In addition to more than 1,000 manufacturing plants—which produce jeeps, spark plugs, chemicals, and other products—Toledo is a major center for the glass industry. Owens-Illinois, Libby-Owens-Ford, and Owens-Corning Fiberglas manufacture a variety of glass products in Toledo.

South of Toledo, on the Maumee River, is the site of the *Battle of Fallen Timbers.* On 20 August 1794, American troops under Major General Anthony Wayne decisively defeated the Indians under Little Turtle. The next year a treaty was signed that opened the Northwest Territory to white settlers. If you go to Fallen Timbers—so called because a fierce storm knocked down trees at the then-forested site—you can stand on the same rock where it is said Little Turtle stood to rally his forces against General Wayne. For further information on the region, contact the Greater Toledo Office of Tourism and Conventions, 218 Huron Street, Toledo, Ohio 43604 (telephone 419-321-6404).

Toledo, Ohio, to Detroit, Michigan, 60 miles, I-75

Interstate 75 north takes us from Toledo to *Detroit* (population, 1,089,000)—Motor City—capital of the U.S. auto industry. Detroit is the birthplace of mass production and the producer of nearly 25 percent of the nation's automobiles, trucks, and tractors. It was perhaps an element of chance that Detroit achieved such prominence as an automobile center. Several other cities also produced automobiles, or horseless carriages, as they were called, but Henry Ford lived in Detroit and it was he who introduced the assembly line, which, with standardization of parts, permitted mass production. John Gunther, in *Inside U.S.A.*, said "More than any other American region, except possibly New England, [the Middle West] represents the full flowering of the 'gadget mind.' Most American boys, and in particular those from midwest farms, are born mechanics; they can do anything with their hands. Out of this and much else has come what Detroit, let us say, symbolizes better than any other American city—the assembly line and mass production." The growth of Detroit was chiefly dependent on the automobile industry and its allies and its economy is still based on the automobile.

The inbound drive along the interstate provides more than the subtle shadings of Motor City: low-slung buildings of auto suppliers and the leviathan Rouge manufacturing complex of the Ford Motor Company, the largest industrial complex in the world.

Detroit, whose roots are French, was founded by Antoine de la Mothe Cadillac in 1701 at "le place du detroit," the strait between

Lake St. Clair and Lake Erie along the Detroit River. He was determined to block British expansion into the fur-rich lands to the north and west. After the French and Indian War, Detroit became British, then was taken over by the Americans in 1796.

Lately Detroit has been locked in a battle with a force more insidious than English redcoats: the post-industrial malaise. Unique economic and geographic factors have left Detroit in an especially bleak condition. Competition from foreign automobiles has torn the spine from the local economy. While other cities retained downtown commerce, plentiful land beyond Detroit's boundaries hastened the rise of suburban economic centers like Southfield. This resulted in modern splashy suburban communities backed by a shell that was once downtown Detroit.

It is along the waterfront that the city has been winning its greatest victories. The river is the focal point of the city's hopes for urban revitalization; it is also the destination of choice when people are simply out for fun. Though the city has a reputation for violence, the vast majority of crimes take place in Detroit's outlying neighborhoods. The riverfront is not only prospering, it is safe.

For a perspective on the river and the city it embraces, head up to the observation deck of the Westin Hotel (telephone 313-568-8000). The tallest building in the *Renaissance Center,* the "glass canister set" dominates the waterfront skyline. From the seventy-second floor, Detroit spreads out in a vast, green–brown checkerboard sprawl of flattened smokestacks and, on the river's far side, is verdant southwestern Ontario.

From the downtown area Detroit connects with Windsor in Canada by both bridge and tunnel. From the Renaissance Center, you can see *Belle Isle Park,* the country's largest city island park. Belle Isle is a haven for bikers, runners, and golfers. It offers many attractions, including a conservatory, an aquarium, a nature center, a zoo, and a museum that depicts Great Lakes maritime history. Detroit also has a historical museum at 5401 Woodward Avenue; Historic Fort Wayne, at 6325 West Jefferson Avenue; the Motown Museum, at 2648 West Grand Boulevard; and a Museum of African American History at 301 Frederick Douglass.

Renaissance Center, Detroit, Michigan. Photograph courtesy of the Michigan Travel Bureau.

The Metropolitan Detroit Convention and Visitor's Bureau maintains a twenty-four hour directory of events (telephone 313-298-6262) and distributes free brochures and maps (2 Jefferson Avenue, Detroit, Michigan 48226; telephone, 313-259-4333).

The nation's largest indoor–outdoor museum complex is the *Henry Ford Museum and Greenfield Village,* 20900 Oakwood Boulevard, Dearborn (313-271-1620). Take I-94 to Oakwood Boulevard exit. The 12-acre museum focuses on American industrial development between 1800 and 1950. A special exhibit takes an in-depth look at the world the car transformed. The village, set on a 240-acre site, encompasses more than eighty historic buildings, a train, and a paddle-wheel riverboat.

The world headquarters of Ford Motor Company is at Dearborn. Cadillac Motor Car Division is nearby. Ford Road (Route 153) goes west through Dearborn, past Henry Ford Community College and the University of Michigan Henry Ford Museum. Edsel Ford Freeway is I-94 north. I-75 north is Chrysler Freeway, which leads to Pontiac. The Silverdome is at Pontiac, near I-75/Route 59 Interchange. South of the city center I-75 is Fisher Freeway (Fisher Bodies Division of General Motors). Mack Avenue (Mack trucks) leads from Grand Boulevard near the city center to Grosse Pointe Woods. Plymouth Road goes west from Dearborn toward Ann Arbor. Dodge Brothers State Park is west of Pontiac. The International Airport is at Romulus, in the southwest section of the metro area. Take the I-275 bypass to I-94 and then east.

The *Eastern Farmer's Market* (2934 Russell, 313-833-1560), in operation since 1892, is of special interest. Mammoth ethnic murals decorate the outside walls of the market, which is the largest of its kind in the United States. Visitors can bargain with vendors for fresh vegetables, meats, cheeses, and flowers. Tuesday and Saturday are retail market days.

In the downtown area we will see the *Detroit People Mover.* You can enjoy a breath-taking view of the city as you travel on one of the most technologically advanced systems in the world. The Detroit People Mover is an enclosed, computerized transportation system that uses magnetic force for propulsion and braking. It takes only fourteen minutes to travel the 2.94 miles of track.

The Detroit–Windsor Tunnel (100 E. Jefferson Avenue) is accessible from all freeways. It is an engineering wonder, a 5,160-foot tunnel under the Detroit River, connecting downtown Detroit to downtown Windsor, Ontario.

△ *Day Six*

DETROIT TO BENTON HARBOR, MICHIGAN

Detroit to Ann Arbor, Michigan, 40 miles, I-94

Leave downtown Detroit by way of I-94 West, through Dearborn, by way of Ypsilanti, to Ann Arbor. It is about 10 miles from Renaissance Center to the I-275 beltline, then another 30 miles to Ann Arbor.

Ypsilanti (population, 23,300) was named, in 1832, for a Greek revolutionary general, Demitrius Ypsilanti, who gained fame by holding the entire Turkish army at bay and escaping without loss of any of his own 300 soldiers. Ypsilanti is home to numerous industries and to Eastern Michigan University.

Ann Arbor (population, 107,966) is named for its tree-shaded sites. It is a cosmopolitan city with a year-round schedule of performing arts and educational activities. The *University of Michigan,* originally in Detroit, moved to a 1,300-acre campus in Ann Arbor in 1837. The university has been the primary influence in the growth and life of Ann Arbor. Its museums and libraries are major points of interest. Among these are the Kelsey Museum of Archaeology, 434 South State Street; Matthaei Botanical Gardens, 1800 North Dixboro Road; University of Michigan Exhibit Museum, 1109 Geddes Avenue; and University of Michigan Museum of Art, 525 South State Street. The Ford Nuclear Reactor, 2301 Bonisteel Boulevard, is on the north campus. It was built as a memorial to the University of Michigan's war dead. The lab

Detroit, Michigan, to Benton Harbor, Michigan

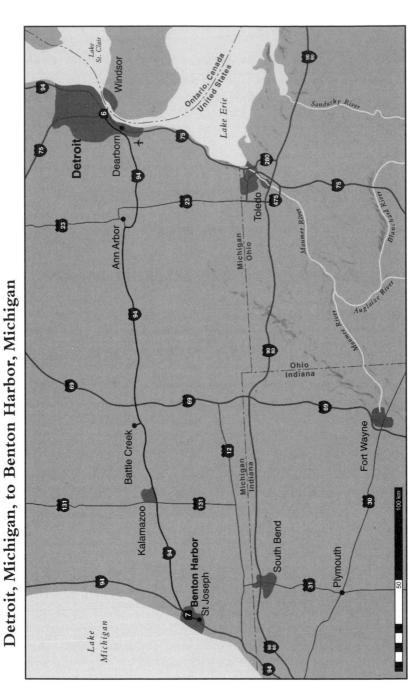

houses a 2-million-watt nuclear reactor and other facilities for research aimed at peace-time use of nuclear energy. Take U.S. 23 to Plymouth Road exit on the north campus (313-764-6220).

The University of Michigan is one of the largest and most highly regarded in the United States. Its colleges cover almost all professions and its athletic teams are among the best.

Other attractions in or near Ann Arbor include Cobblestone Farm, 2781 Packard Road; Domino's Farms, 30 Frank Lloyd Wright Drive; and Kerrytown, 407 North Fifth Avenue. *Cobblestone Farm* includes an 1844 Classical Revival cobblestone farmhouse, a wooded kitchen ell, an 1837 log cabin, and an earthen barn. Take U.S. 23 to Washtenow Road exit, south on Platt Road, then west on Packard Road (313-994-2928).

Domino's Farms is the world headquarters of Domino's Pizza. This farm complex houses the Domino's Pizza Classic Cars Collection Museum, the Frank Lloyd Wright Museum, and a petting zoo. Take U.S. 23 to exit 41, 5 miles northeast of Ann Arbor (313-995-4258).

Kerrytown, between Fourth and Fifth avenues, adjacent to Farmer's Market, is a group of restored nineteenth-century buildings that house a variety of specialty shops and restaurants (313-662-4221).

Jackson to Battle Creek, Michigan, 45 miles, I-94

After touring the campus, leave Ann Arbor and continue west on I-94. It is about 30 miles to *Jackson* (population, 37,700) through level to gently rolling, sparsely wooded farmlands. The area is noted for the production of fruit, vegetables, crude oil, and various tools and parts associated with the automobile industry. The Republican Party was founded in Jackson in 1854; a tablet marks the site. Today the city is best known as an industrial and transportation center.

MARSHALL, MICHIGAN

Continue west on I-94 to *Marshall* (population, 7,200). Marshall is lucky. It was settled in 1831 by New York State land speculators but has remained an attractive small city. The Department of the Interior has designated a large chunk of Marshall, including about 800 buildings, a National Historical Landmark District.

Marshall makes Middle West seem like the sweetest place on Earth. The wide streets are lined with heroic tulip, maple, and pine trees, which are home to svelte-looking black squirrels. Plush stretches of green grass release a pleasant lawny fragrance. Overhead birds twitter, warble, and chirp.

Marshall is defined by its houses. Set well back from the sidewalk, with plenty of room on either side, they evoke a free, more ample way of life, when families were large, front porches could accommodate multitudes, and interiors offered the mysteries of nooks and crannies. Its houses have towers, gables, Gothic windows, widow's walks, campaniles, bargeboards, tracery, lacy woodwork trim, porticoes, columns, and front, side, and rear porches.

White frame houses are dwindling in number. Marshall's homeowners have returned to the rich, extroverted palette of the nineteenth century, correcting the historical mistake of a century ago, when America decided to imitate New England and paint its houses chalk white. Marshall houses are cream-colored with chocolate trim, canary yellow with black shutters, blue-gray and royal blue, teal and white, pink and red. Pleasing in itself, color gives sharp relief to architectural detail.

At one time Marshall was proposed as the site of the state capital but Lansing was chosen instead. Marshall is also known as the site of the founding of the Michigan public school system, a center of railroading, and a patent medicine mecca. Thirty-five historical markers dot the city which boasts of more than 1,200 nineteenth-century commercial and residential structures. Thanks to the collapse of the railroad boom, Marshall's appearance hasn't changed greatly over the years. The community has an unusual number of excellent examples of Greek and Gothic Revival, Italianate, and Queen Anne architecture. Marshall also played a role in precipitating the Civil War. It was the site of the Crosswhite Case in 1846, a case instrumental in the creation of the Fugitive Slave Act.

Marshall is built around a center circle dominated by a Greek Revival fountain. *National House Inn* is on the circle. Built in

1835, it is Michigan's oldest operating inn. It was also a station on the underground railroad before and during the Civil War. The inn is a period hostel but with modern conveniences. For reservations write National House Inn, 102 South Parkview, Marshall, Michigan, 49068 or call 616-781-7374.

The most famous building in Marshall is *Honolulu House,* built in 1860—a tropical fantasy painted ivory, red, and three shades of green. Now a museum and headquarters of the Marshall Historical Society, the house is open daily from mid-May to October (616-781-8544). For a tour of Marshall's historic homes contact the Marshall Chamber of Commerce (800-877-5163).

Schuler's, perhaps Michigan's best restaurant, is a family-operated restaurant that was started by Albert Schuler as a combined cigar store and lunch counter more than eighty years ago. The original restaurant had only twenty seats but was more prosperous than the cigar business. In 1924 Mr. Schuler bought the Royal Hotel in downtown Marshall and moved the twenty-seat restaurant to it. He renamed the hotel The Schuler. His son Win joined him in the business and by 1946 the restaurant had been enlarged to seat 200 people. It now seats 500 and often has waiting lines. The restaurant has stayed in the family; Win's son and grandsons are now in charge. They have two other restaurants, in Jackson and Stevensville, but the one in Marshall is the restaurant where it all began. Schuler's is a state pride. The ceiling beams in the restaurants are known for sayings painted in English script for the amusement of guests. Famous quotes from Emerson and Longfellow are among them. Mary Alice Powell, food editor for the *Toledo Blade,* in a recent article wrote:

> Our neighboring state to the north is known for juicy and tart cherry pies, delicious Lake Superior Whitefish, apple dumplings, huckleberry shortcake, fried pheasant, venison roasts. And Schuler restaurants. In an eating-out world of fast food drive-throughs, pizza, and tacos, it's nice to know that four generations of one Michigan family stuck to their guns, saute pans and roasters to compete in a slower lane with American fare served American style.

We fully agree and plan to come back to Schuler's, 115 South Eagle Street, Marshall, Michigan, 49068; 616-781-0600).

Marshall's Town Hall, on the southeast corner of Michigan Avenue and old U.S. 27 on the circle across from the Brooks Memorial Fountain, is in a building that started as a stone barn, built in 1857. It later operated as a livery stable and stagecoach company, before being restored and becoming the Town Hall.

BATTLE CREEK, MICHIGAN

From Marshall it is 10 miles to *Battle Creek* (population, 46,339), Cereal Capital of the World. Battle Creek is midway between Detroit and Chicago, an advantageous site for any enterprise. Although the city's early renown was based on health (the Battle Creek Sanitarium) and cereal (Kellogg's, Post, Ralston-Purina), it is "not just for breakfast anymore." The city's aggressively marked Industrial Park is known throughout the world and includes major representatives from Japan, Germany, and England, as well as a U.S. Customs Port of Entry and Foreign Trade Zone.

Kellogg Company's worldwide leadership of its industry stems from the invention of flaked cereal in 1894—by accident—at the Battle Creek Sanitarium. The "San," an internationally known Seventh Day Adventist hospital and health spa, offered its rich and famous patients a regimen of exercise and fresh air, plus a strict diet that prohibited caffeine, alcohol, tobacco, and meat. Sanitarium superintendent Dr. John Harvey Kellogg and Will Keith Kellogg, his younger brother and business manager, invented many grain-based foods, including a coffee substitute, a type of granola, and peanut butter. They conducted a series of experiments to develop good-tasting substitutes for the hard and tasteless bread on the San's menu. Wheat was cooked, forced through granola rollers, then rolled into long sheets of dough. One day after cooking the wheat, the men were called away. Although the wheat was rather stale when they returned, the brothers decided to see what would happen when the tempered grain was forced through the rollers. Instead of the usual long sheets of dough, each wheat berry was flattened into a small thin flake. When baked, the flakes tasted crisp and light. Although Will Keith and John Harvey were aware that they had invented a good-tasting food that was easy to prepare, they had no idea that they had also invented a new industry. Sanitarium patients enjoyed the wheat flakes and wanted to continue eating them at home. As a service to former patients, Dr. Kellogg started the Sanitas Nut Food Company. He put his younger brother in charge of the small business to produce the cereal for mail orders. Entrepreneurs quickly profited from copying and retailing flaked wheat cereal. By 1902, more than forty factories had sprung up in the shadow of the San, taking advantage of its reputation to advertise their products as health foods.

Meanwhile, W.K., as Will Keith was known, continued his own experiments, developing the process for flaking corn in 1898. Seeing the potential of cereal products, and recognizing his brother's lack of interest in expanding their own food company, W.K. left his job of twenty-five years to go into business for himself. For the first time he could use his own ideas for manufacturing and marketing his product to the public. He decided to introduce corn flakes with malt flavoring to distinguish his cereal from the competition. On 1 April 1906, less than one week before his forty-sixth birthday, he formed the Battle Creek Toasted Corn Flake Company, renamed Kellogg Company in 1922. The company grew quickly. All-Bran was introduced in 1916, Rice Krispies in 1928. Today, Kellogg produces more than forty different cereals in sixteen countries, and markets its products in more than 130 countries. Kellogg Company's most advanced cereal manufacturing facility, Building 100, began operations in 1988.

Both W. K. Kellogg and C. W. Post, the cereal pioneers, lived and died in Battle Creek. They are buried in Oak Hill Cemetery on South Street.

To get to downtown Battle Creek from I-94, take Exit 98 and turn north on I-194/State Route 66, and follow it to Michigan Avenue. Turn right and it is just a short distance to the Kellogg plant on the left side. The plant is housed in a very modern building with beautiful grounds and a receptionist in the lobby.

Just across the street from the Kellogg plant is McCamley Place, a downtown specialty complex with more than thirty retail shops, express eateries and sit-down restaurants, and special events and

Kellogg Plant, Battle Creek, Michigan. Photograph by P. P. Karan.

live entertainment. It is open Monday through Saturday, 10:00 a.m. to 9:00 p.m.; Sunday, noon till 5:00 p.m. For information concerning events call 616-961-3090.

The Fort Custer Industrial Park occupies 2,400 acres of the former Fort Custer Military Reservation on West Dickman Road. At 15501 West Dickman Road is the *Fort Custer National Cemetery,* a 770-acre cemetery that includes graves of several German World War II prisoners of war and the grave of an unknown soldier. One hundred and fifty American flags line the entrance and nearby are each of the fifty state flags. The cemetery office is open 8:00 a.m. to 4:30 p.m. (616-731-4164). Northwest of the cemetery on the West Dickman Road near Augusta is the entrance to Fort Custer Recreational Area. This 3,000-acre area, between the Kalamazoo River and a state military training site, has four lakes, rolling meadows, soggy wetlands, and abundant woods.

In Battle Creek at 74 North Washington Avenue is *Battle Creek Federal Center.* Once the site of Dr. John Harvey Kellogg's world-famous Battle Creek Sanitarium, this facility now houses several government and military offices. Some artifacts from the sanitarium and items owned by Dr. Kellogg are displayed in the lobbies of the building. The center was also known as Percy Jones Army Hospital from 1942 to 1953. Some 120,000 GI's were treated here. The building is on the National Register of Historic Places because of its importance in the field of medical science. Prearranged guided tours are available (616-961-7015).

Other places of interest include the Battle Creek Art Center, 265 East Emmett Street; Binder Park Zoo, 7400 Division Drive, south of I-94; Kimball House Museum, 196 Capital Avenue Northeast; Kimball Pines Park, 115 East Michigan; and Kingman Museum of Natural History, 175 Limit Street, West Michigan at Twentieth. Battle Creek has several large shopping centers, excellent hotels and motels and other tourist facilities.

A wide variety of businesses and restaurants line both sides of Columbia Avenue, the primary Battle Creek business loop, off I-94. Capital and Michigan avenues are two main strips that run through downtown and into several neighborhood shopping districts.

Battle Creek to Benton Harbor, Michigan, 45 miles, I-94

Leave Battle Creek and head west again on I-94 to Kalamazoo, about 20 miles away. Our route crosses level to gently rolling, semi-wooded farmlands noted for production of fruit, vegetables, and livestock. The climate in this area is tempered by Lake Michigan, making it ideal for apples, cherries, peaches, pears, plums, berries, potatoes, sugar beets, grapes, hay, and pasture. The area is also famous for celery, a crop that does well in the black earth of the old lakebed. Wood and paper products are important here and Georgia-Pacific has a paper mill just east of Kalamazoo on State Route 96. The town of Parchment adjoins Kalamazoo on the north.

KALAMAZOO, MICHIGAN

Kalamazoo (population, 79,722) is home to Western Michigan University, Kalamazoo College, Nazareth College, and Kalamazoo Valley Community College. It is also the headquarters of Upjohn Company and visitors may tour their pharmaceutical facility. Vineyards and wineries are nearby and they also offer tours and samples.

Kalamazoo is in a scenic area with numerous streams, lakes, and fruit-tree- and vineyard-covered hillsides. There are more than sixty public parks in Kalamazoo County, many with beaches, trout streams, and honking geese. James Fenimore Cooper especially liked the area now called Cooper's Glen, site of the Kalamazoo Nature Center. Here you can visit 640 acres of trails and botanical gardens. The area has sixteen public golf courses.

The *Celery Flats Interpretive Center,* South Westnedge and Garden Lane in Portage, has tours, museums, and artifacts that illustrate the region's heritage as a celery farming center (616-329-4522).

Many areas of Kalamazoo have historical buildings and sites. Vine, Stuart, and South street neighborhoods are designated historic districts and offer views of varied architectural styles, including Gothic, Italianate, Greek Revival, Sullivanesque, Queen Anne, Art Deco, and others.

BENTON HARBOR, MICHIGAN

Leave Kalamazoo and continue west on I-94 for the last 35 miles of this tour. Our route is still through a fruit- and vegetable-growing region, which ends at *Benton Harbor* (population 14,707) on the shore of Lake Michigan. St. Joseph (population, 9,622) is separated from Benton Harbor only by the St. Joseph River.

In 1960 Benton Harbor had nearly 20,000 residents and was well-known for its canneries and factories that produced steel castings, wood veneer, and machinery. It is in the heart of a fruit-growing and vacation resort area, but its declining population reflects the state of the economy throughout the industrial Middle West. Many businesses are closed.

Epilogue

Our tour from Washington, D.C., to Benton Harbor, Michigan, has given us a glimpse of the physical, cultural, and economic diversity of the area from historic places on the Atlantic coast and the Piedmont to the glaciated lake plains of the Midwest. Between the East and the Midwest we have traversed the very unique Appalachian region.

PART THREE

Resources

△ Hints to the Traveler

Most of these roads go through mountainous areas which are subject to snow and ice earlier than low-lying areas, and to fog at any time. If you go in winter, be prepared and flexible enough to change your plans.

These areas, especially the Skyline Drive, are spectacular in autumn, but this is not a well-kept secret. On a weekend in prime "leaf-peeper" season, you may have to wait in line to get on the Skyline Drive.

In addition to comfortable clothing and shoes you should include a sweater or jacket and a light raincoat even in summer. The weather can be changeable.

VISA or Mastercards are now accepted at most hotels, restaurants, and shops.

If you require a particular type of film for your camera buy it in advance.

Medicines and prescriptions or special needs? You should take care of these needs before starting the excursion.

August Weather

	Charleston	Pittsburgh	Cleveland	Detroit
Temperature °F				
Normals				
Daily Maximum	84.2	81.1	80.3	81.5
Daily Minimum	63.1	60.1	60.5	59.4
Monthly Average	73.7	70.6	70.4	70.5
Extremes				
Record High	100	97	102	97
Record Low	41	39	38	38
% of Possible Sunshine	55	56	63	69
Precipitation (inches)				
Normal	4.15	3.31	3.38	3.21
Maximum Monthly	10.45	7.56	8.96	7.83
Minimum Monthly	0.66	0.78	0.53	0.72

Note: Statistics above are averages. Extremes may be encountered, especially in the winter months when heavy snow or sub-zero temperatures may occur in the mountains or the Great Lakes area. In summer, air conditioning in buildings sometimes warrants a sweater.

△ Suggested Readings

American Automobile Association. Guidebooks for each state and region. Published annually.
    Contain a tremendous amount of information for travelers. Geography, history, hotel and motel descriptions, restaurants, and attractions.

Atwood, Wallace W. *The Physiographic Provinces of North America.* New York: Ginn and Co., 1940.
    One of the classic physical descriptions of the North American continent.

Buckeye North. Special Publication by Erie County (Ohio) Visitors Bureau, Sandusky, Ohio, 1991.
    Description of the Sandusky-Lake Erie attractions and accommodations including the wineries.

Detroit Visitor's Guide. Metropolitan Detroit Convention & Visitors Bureau, 1991.
    A complete guide with maps and information about attractions, transportation, history, and accommodations.

Fenneman, Nevin M. *Physiography of Eastern United States.* New York: McGraw-Hill Book Co., 1938.
    This is the classic physical geography of the region.

Frye, Keith. *Roadside Geology of Virginia.* Missoula: Mountain Press Publishing Co., 1986, 1990.
    Excellent geological description of the Shenandoah Valley and National Park area.

Hunt, Charles B. *Natural Regions of the United States and Canada.* San Francisco: W. H. Freeman and Co., 1974.
    Good general description.

Michigan Travel Planner. Special Publication by Michigan Travel Bureau, Lansing, 1991. Published annually.
Maps and information concerning attractions, accommodations, climate, and traffic laws. Includes an overview of communities and a list of contacts for more information.

Noble, Allen G. "Landscape of Piety/Landscape of Profit: The Amish-Mennonite and Derived Landscapes of Northeastern Ohio." *The East Lakes Geographer*, Vol. 21 (1986), pp. 34–38.
Description and photographs of Amish-Mennonite settlements in Ohio.

Raitz, Karl B. and Richard Ulack with Thomas R. Leinbach. *Appalachia, A Regional Geography: Land, People, and Development.* Boulder & London: Westview Press, 1984.
General descriptions with extensive bibliography.

Smith, J. Russell and Phillips, M. Ogden. *North America: Its People and the Resources, Development and Prospects of the Continent as the Home of Man.* New York: Harcourt, Brace and Co., 1940.
This text along with an earlier version by Smith is a classic. Explains why cities and regions developed as they have.

The Holmes County Traveler, Vol. 3, No. 1, March–April, 1991.
A Special Publication by Holman County, Ohio, with much information about the Amish-Mennonite Community.

Thornbury, William D. *Regional Geomorphology of the United States.* New York: John Wiley & Sons, 1965.
For the serious student of landforms. Detailed description.

Van Diver, Bradford B. *Roadside Geology of Pennsylvania.* Missoula: Mountain Press Publishing Company, 1990.
Has excellent description of the rock structures in the Pittsburgh area.

West Virginia, It's You. Special Publication by Bell Atlantic Specialty Guides, Bethesda, 1991. Information furnished by West Virginia Division of Tourism and Parks. Published annually.
An excellent guide to attractions and accommodations.

White, C. Langdon et al. *Regional Geography of Anglo-America*, 5th Ed. Englewood Cliffs, N.J.: Prentice-Hall, 1979.
Good general description of area covered in this traverse.

Zelinsky, Wilbur. *The Cultural Geography of the United States.* Englewood Cliffs, N.J.: Prentice-Hall, 1973.
Especially valuable for the foreign visitor. Attempts to explain some of the complexities of American people and way of life.

△ Index